I Love My
Workbook

7 Simple Guided Steps So You Can Completely Stop Binge Eating
and Overeating, Reach Your Goal Weight, and Leave Shame, Guilt,
and Food Obsession Behind You

Table Of Contents

Principles And Promises

Never Binge Again™ is a radically different approach to overcoming overeating, and this workbook will help you embrace and integrate all its powerful principles. You'll learn to:

→ **Eat Healthy without Relying on Willpower**: You'll see how to rely on rules vs. guidelines for key food decisions because guidelines seriously tax your willpower, and you've only got so much! As you work your way through this book, starting with the very first exercise, you'll find yourself SO much less drained by constant decision making about food, and that energy can be put to other, more important, healthier uses in your life!

→ **Find Freedom from Food Obsession**: As you eliminate and automate difficult food decisions, you'll discover that the mental obsession with food should lift. After all, no difficult decisions to make means there's nothing to think about, right? You can finally put your mind to better uses, including simply being present, mindful, and aware.

→ **Discover the Body You Were Meant to Live In**: As food becomes less and less of an issue in your life, your body should gradually shed the excess weight you've been holding until you reach a natural, comfortable weight.

→ **Escape the Tyranny of "Emotional Eating"**: Never again feel compelled to put bad food in your body just because you don't like the way you feel!

→ **Break Free from the Diet Mentality:** Find sustainable habits you can live with for a lifetime!

→ **Uncover Your Most Personal and Sustainable Motivation:** Get BOTH a short-term boost in motivation AND the power to carry you through the long run! All personalized to your specific needs.

→ **Reclaim Your Power:** To this point you've been letting your Lizard Brain (lower brain) control you. It's time to take back the reins and show the Lizard who's boss!

→ **End the War on Food:** Ever fought a war with a bagel, donut, chocolate bar, piece of pizza, or dish of pasta...and lost? Are you exhausted from constantly trying to wage a "war on food" in your own head... where YOU are the primary casualty? See how to declare the war over once and for all so you can find peace again.

→ **Successfully Defend Yourself Against Big Food, Big Advertising, and Big Addiction Treatment:** In today's economy there are billions of dollars targeted at your Lizard Brain. Big Food engineers "food like substances" intended to hit our bliss point without giving us enough nutrition to be satisfied. Billions of dollars go into researching and manufacturing hyperpalatable concentrations of starch, sugar, fat, oil, salt, and excitotoxins that break our hungry and full meters until it becomes virtually impossible to "eat when you're hungry and stop when you're full." Big Advertising then tells us we can't live without this junk—and if you think advertising doesn't affect you, think again because it affects you MORE when your sales resistance is down! Then Big Addiction says we can't quit even if we want to, the best we can do is abstain one day at a time. It's a perfect storm for overeating, but there's a simple defense against all of it, and we'll help you build one to protect you where you're most vulnerable.

REMEMBER: You don't have to rush through this book! In fact, you'll get the most out of it if you go slowly. Every step along the way is designed to improve your relationship with food, and it may be helpful to repeat some of them in order to solidify understanding and mastery as you go along.

ALSO: This book is a companion book for—*and assumes you have access to*—my bestselling book Never Binge Again *(3,050+ ratings on Amazon and over a half million copies in distribution).* Only a basic familiarity with the concepts is required, but as you go through *this* workbook you will benefit tremendously from reviewing the relevant sections of Never Binge Again. It's available for free on Kindle, Nook, and PDF at www.NeverBingeAgain.com.

FINALLY: Throughout this book I refer to audio examples. I've published hundreds of recorded sessions via my podcast over the years. We've taken some of the best of these and indexed them to the exercises in the workbook so that you know what to listen to when you're immersed in them. The indexed and timestamped example audios can be found at www.WorkbookExamples.com.

Pre-Assessment – Test Your Current Food Addiction Level

Before we get started, let's do a quick assessment of where you stand with your eating. Just go to www.HowBigIsMyFoodProblem.com and take the three minute quiz, then write down your score below. You'll be glad you did because you'll be able to go back and take it again after you're done to see your progress. No matter how high your score, the exercises in this book, starting with the very first one, should seriously help you take control of your eating forever. Take the test now, write down your score, then go through the workbook at your own pace and come back to take the test again. You will likely see a dramatic improvement. *(TAKE THE QUIZ AND WRITE DOWN YOUR SCORE BELOW):*

→ **STARTING FOOD PROBLEM SCORE:** ____ *(Write your score here)*

Chapter 1

One Simple Rule Can Change Your Life!

Overview

What if I said you could radically change your relationship with food, dramatically improve your health, and replace feelings of hopelessness and powerlessness about food with confidence, hope, and enthusiasm... by creating just ONE simple Food Rule? What if, with the stroke of a pen, you could in this very first exercise do something that literally changed your life?

People DO have such moments. Sometimes, with the aid of a few simple questions and a philosophy they believe in, people are finally ready to accept an insight and/or intuitive knowledge they've been keeping from themselves for decades, and then, EVERYTHING changes.

And what if you've been trying TOO hard to fix your overeating problem. What if the solution were a LOT simpler than your Lizard Brain wants you to know?

What if all it really came down to was slowly turning your ship around with ONE simple rule, without worrying about weight loss for the moment, and without putting so much pressure into a "diet mentality" that inevitably fails time and again?

I know it's probably hard to believe from where you sit right now, but literally hundreds of thousands of readers have proven this can and does happen. As you go through the workbook, you'll understand why the clarity, commitment, and confidence which congeals around your first rule can make ALL the difference in the world.

I'll explain why this works so well as we go along...

But for now, what do you have to lose?

➔ **Nobody is going to tell you what to eat...**

➔ **Nobody is going to tell you what NOT to eat either!**

➔ **You can change your rule at any time!** You'll present your One Simple Food Rule to your Pig as if it were set in stone forever, but YOU can change it any time with forethought and consideration. It's kind of like telling a two-year-old "You can never cross the street without holding my hand. Never ever (ever!)" You know you're going to change that rule for the kid in a few years when they have the maturity to learn how to look both ways before they cross, but at the moment they have to BELIEVE the rule is forever because it's not safe for them to think otherwise. You don't even want the image of jumping into the street by themselves in their mind, so you tell them NEVER. Same thing with your Pig... you don't want to allow your Lizard Brain the luxury of even thinking breaking your One Simple Food Rule is remotely possible, so you tell it the rule is forever.

→ **There'll no reason to punish yourself if you make a mistake.** I will help you release excess guilt and negative self-talk, which only make matters worse. See, the appropriate role for guilt in the psyche is kind of like the appropriate role for physical pain when you touch a hot stove. You WANT to feel the pain for a minute, so you can pay attention and make plans to avoid touching it again. But you don't want to say "I'm a pathetic hot stove toucher, I might as well put my whole hand down on the stove now!" Just figure out what went wrong, get up, and try again. Commit with perfection but forgive yourself with dignity. Getting overly involved with guilt beyond this point is the Pig's attempt to make you feel too weak to resist the next binge.

→ **Your rule won't be too restrictive or burdensome.** We want to find something you can actually do. It should NOT create too dramatic of a caloric or nutritional deficit, because this can trigger the irrational perception of famine in your brain. And if your brain thinks you live in an environment where food and nutrition are scarce, it will eventually force you to be less discriminating and instruct you to hoard food when it perceives it is once again available.

→ **We are going to experiment with this one rule for just 10 days.**

So if you know from the outset that one simple food rule can make ALL the difference, that the rule is entirely up to you, that you can change it at any time, that you won't allow yourself to get too involved with excessive guilt if you make a mistake, and that you're going to re-evaluate it in just 10 days... then why in the world wouldn't you at least try to make ONE?

In just a moment I'm going to give you a few examples and ask you a few questions to help you find just the right rule for yourself. But before I do, I want to ask you to DO something you may consider strange for the moment...

I want you to go someplace private, take a deep breath, and hold this book to your heart.

I know that's weird, but it will help put you in the right mindset to find the most meaningful rule. I want to enlist your unconscious mind to connect this book to your heart in the deepest way so you might be more open to loving yourself with one simple commitment than ever before. I want you to begin with the understanding this is a sacred exercise, even though it's extremely practical and logical on the surface. I want you to be open to changing your life.

Don't skip this please, even if it feels crazy.

Some people will say they can't find enough love for themselves to do this. That's OK. If that's you, hold the book to your heart and take a few deep breaths while you imagine the love which I myself put into this book. Lean on me at first if you need to. But do it.

It's OK if this feels emotional. It's OK if it feels stupid. Do it anyway.

Now, don't get me wrong, this will NOT be a touchy-feely book. Rather, it's an extremely practical approach to help you ruthlessly dominate the inner enemy you've been fighting all these years. I PROMISE I won't make you dig deep into your past or mislead you into thinking you need to solve all your emotional problems to stop overeating. This is a VERY practical workbook. But doing this one "silly" exercise before you choose your first rule will help you take it more seriously. It will make it mean more to you.

So, go hold the book to your heart and take a few deep breaths.

Did you do it? Good!

Introductory Exercise) Write down any thoughts, feelings, insights, and/or observations about holding the book to your heart here. Both *positive* and *negative* thoughts, feelings, insights, and observations are allowed!

_____

_____

_____

_____

_____

_____

_____

_____

Creating One Simple Rule

You goal in this section is to create the SIMPLEST rule possible to start turning your ship around and heading in the right direction. The leading question is **"What is the SIMPLEST rule you could follow which you KNOW would make a big difference in how you eat, but which doesn't feel too burdensome, restrictive, or depriving?"**

It doesn't matter that your Pig says it will be impossible for you to comply. It doesn't matter if it jumps up and down and screams you've failed a million times before, and there's therefore absolutely no use in trying again. It doesn't matter if you were binge eating literally five seconds before you picked up this workbook.

Examples of successful rules people have made in the past include:

➔ **Moderation and Portion Control Rules**

  » I'll never eat bread more than two days per Calendar Week again

  » I'll never go back for seconds again. I know a guy who ONLY ate at fast food restaurants and jump-started his 150-pound weight loss with this one rule!

  » I'll never eat pretzels outside of a major league baseball park.

➔ **Rules that Add Healthy Behaviors**

  » I'll always drink two glasses of water before each meal.

  » I'll always walk for ten minutes before sitting down at my computer for the first time.

  » I always write down a hypothetical food plan for the next day before I go to bed. This helps people head off trouble spots as they think through what they're facing tomorrow. Please note it says "hypothetical." The goal is to think through the next day, not to create something you have to comply with 100%.

➔ **Elimination Rules**

  » I will never eat anything which tastes sweet again besides whole fruit, berries, and stevia.

  » I will never buy food at a drive through again.

➔ **Eating Behavior Support Rules**

  » I'll never eat in front of a screen again.

  » I'll never eat in the car again.

  » I'll never eat standing up again.

  » I'll always put my fork down between bites.

So...

Close your eyes for a minute and think about it...

Exercise 1A) "What is the SIMPLEST rule you could follow which you KNOW would make a big difference in how you eat, but which doesn't feel too burdensome, restrictive, or depriving?" Your Pig will immediately say "we don't know" but push beyond this please because if you don't know, nobody does. But you DO know! Remember, you're not making a commitment yet, and even when you do we're going to start with just ten days. (WRITE YOUR ANSWER BELOW)

_____

_____

_____

_____

_____

_____

_____

Criteria:

→ **Your one simple rule should include the words "never again" or "always."** Otherwise your Pig will think you don't mean business. Remember: YOU can change the rule at any time, but your Pig must think it's set in stone for eternity. *(Note: You use the words "never again" to lock down Conditional rules too. For example, "I will never again eat chocolate on anything but a Saturday and/or Sunday.")*

→ **Your rule must NOT overly restrict your calories and/or daily nutrition.** In fact, it's perfectly OK if it will only cause you to feel more in control of food even if it will not cause you to lose any weight at all. We will make adjustments later on for weight loss. But whatever you do, don't set up a situation where you are losing more than a pound or so per week with this first rule. If you do, you run the danger of staying on the feast and famine roller coaster, forever allowing your brain to trigger "emergency food rule overrides" (binges) where it forces you to be less discriminating. In other words, if you're too hungry the rule will be very hard to follow, and we will defeat the purpose.

→ **You are NOT committing to the rule at this time.** Just write down your best guess above.

You may hear your Pig say something like "How the hell are we supposed to know that!?" Listen, if I could tell you straight out what your rule should be, I promise you I would. I want you to succeed. But your Pig has been insisting on following everyone else's advice for years, hasn't it? And, doesn't it eventually just knock down whatever diet guru you follow?

I prefer you take your first and best intuitive guess about this. I find that works VERY well with clients. But if you really feel you need more help in thinking this through, I have a free worksheet called the "Food Plan Creation Worksheet" on my website. Sign up for the reader bonuses and scroll down once you get them until you see it. Just one note – that worksheet guides you to create an entire Food Plan. But I prefer you start with just ONE simple rule. So, follow the per-rule instructions for your most important, first rule only OK? *(The website is www.NeverBingeAgain.com – click the big red button to find the reader bonuses)*

Exercise 1B) In consideration of the criteria above, how might you refine/revise your One Simple Rule, if at all. Are you sure you've left yourself enough to eat? Did you use the words "never again" or "always?" Remember, you are NOT yet committing to the rule, we're still working on it. Re-write your first rule below.

_____

_____

_____

_____

_____

_____

What if You Can't Decide on Just One Rule?

The reason we start with just ONE rule is because it's essential to put some success behind you. Most people who've struggled with overeating for a lifetime feel very beaten down by all the times they've tried and failed. Their Pig's voice has become extremely loud. They feel like a failure and have begun to feel hopeless and powerless to do anything about their problem. That's why we start as simply as possible to prove to their Pig it's weaker than they are. So generally speaking, I like to start people with just ONE rule.

That said...

Exercise 1C) If *(and only if)* you're having trouble deciding between two or more rules, list them all below. Skip this exercise if you're pretty sure you know what your one simple rule should be.

(i)

_____

_____

_____

(ii)

_____

_____

_____

(iii)

_____

_____

_____

(iv)

_____

_____

_____

Now, seeing all your potential rules in black and white, does any ONE of them "pop" as the best balance between freedom, ease of implementation, and making a genuinely big difference in your eating and confidence? Circle that rule!

Still struggling? Try projecting yourself out into the future just ten days from now. The idea is to do this one time for each rule, each time imaging you'd adopted that particular rule for ten days. See yourself ten days from now, standing in front of the mirror. As you go through each of the potential rules you're considering, ask yourself how confident you look and feel in the mirror. Is there anything different about your face? The way you're holding yourself? Your skin? I know it's only ten days from now, but look for subtle differences, especially in the way you feel.

Pick the rule which makes you feel MOST confident and happy and circle it.

Remember, even though we're writing your first rule in such a way that your Pig will think it's forever, we're only going to experiment with it for ten days. You'll be able to add, revise, etc. very shortly.

Your Pig will try to prevent you from choosing. It wants to keep you in a state of chaos. It does not want you to have a clear bullseye. It will say ANYTHING and everything it can to do this. Choose anyway. You'll be glad you did!

Without yet committing to your One Simple Rule—*we'll do that at the end of the following motivation section if you choose*—begin simply doing your best to follow it, and notice how your Pig starts Squealing loudly to get you to break it. We're going to methodically deal with *every* last thing your Pig may say shortly, but for now, simply begin to recognize and ignore all the loud and crazy things it says. "Start tomorrow", "You've never succeeded before so you can't possibly succeed now", "You were good all day/week so you can make an exception", etc.

Any voice, thought, feeling, or impulse in your head which suggests you won't, can't, or shouldn't follow your One Simple Rule is your Pig. You CAN and should simply ignore your Pig when you recognize it. Just be sure you're getting enough calories and nutrition and begin to ignore the Pig now. This all becomes a LOT easier once you've amplified your motivation. It's towards this aim we turn next, and you should do this next section at your earliest convenience after choosing your One Simple Rule.

Chapter 2

Enhancing Motivation — Your Big Why!

Within your unconscious mind is a blueprint for success. Whether you know it or not you already have a clear path to your goal inside you. My job is to help you expose, refine, and amplify it.

Within your Pig's unconscious mind, however, is a blueprint for failure. It doesn't want you to see the end goal of this blueprint—what your future will really look like if you keep making the wrong choices *(not committing to ANY rules and eating the Slop your Pig wants you to eat.)* So, it's extremely helpful to thoroughly expose this blueprint too.

In fact, we need to thoroughly expose both blueprints in order to find and amplify your deepest motivation.

Let's begin with your unconscious success blueprint!

Every decision defines a path in your life by influencing both direction and future decisions. Therefore, even one rule can make a giant difference in your life. Take, for example, the rule "I will never go back for seconds again." You may think this wouldn't do much in the way of weight loss and health because it still allows the person to eat anything and everything they want, it only limits volume.

Well, first of all, limiting volume isn't something to be dismissed lightly! Back in the days I was really going to town with my eating, I could easily wolf down 20,000+ calories in a day. It's not that hard to do when you visit seven different drive-throughs! But putting that aside, implementing just one rule like "I will never go back for seconds again" does something else very profound—it begins to restore a sense of control.

See, in the absence of successfully following ANY rules for very long, people begin to feel out of control, helpless, and powerless. As a result, the Pig comes to prominence with "Who-the-f-cares, let's just eat whatever the hell we feel like eating, and as much as we feel like eating too!" But the moment you prove to yourself you can follow even the simplest of rules you've begun to reclaim your power. The feelings of helplessness and powerlessness go away, and in their stead begins to grow a newfound confidence.

That confidence then becomes a positive snowball and the person begins to think "maybe I could do a little more." The guy who proves to himself he can avoid going back for seconds for ten days says to himself "Hmmm... I'm feeling better. Less bloated. More in control. Maybe I'll make another rule that gets me to replace ONE of my drive-through meals with something healthier and lower calorie." So, he creates a second rule a few weeks later that says "I will never eat breakfast at a drive through again."

Before you know it, this becomes a *positive* snowball, he adds another rule or two to moderate sugar, salt, and white flour in his diet, add just a little bit of exercise...and a year later he's lost a ton of weight. But it's not the just the weight he's happy with. In fact, that's become a side benefit. His knees no longer hurt. His skin has cleared up. He's begun being intimate with his wife again. He has more energy. His digestion is a million times better. He gets down on the floor to play with his kids every day. He's more productive at work. He sleeps better. In fact, he feels better across his *entire* life.

Your Big Why is your imagination about what your life will be like in the future if you were to follow your One Simple Rule 100%. I know your Pig will scream that this is impossible, so it's not even worth doing as an exercise. Do it anyway. WHAT IF the Pig was wrong and you were 100% successful in following your rule? What would be different?

We'll start by looking one full year from now.

Exercise 2A) Imagine it's one full year from now. Despite your Pig doing and saying everything it could possibly do and/or say to get you to break your One Simple Rule, you succeeded! In fact, you not only followed your rule 100% for 365 days, you kept at it for ONE FULL YEAR. More importantly, doing so led to a positive snowball of changes over the course of the year which radically improved your life.

TRY TO IMAGINE THE BEST POSSIBLE *(YET STILL BELIEVABLE)* **RESULT!**

Failure is NOT an option in this exercise because in this scenario, <u>success has already been achieved!</u> The right mindset is to consider what might happen if a 900-pound gorilla followed you around and MADE you follow your rules! AND REMEMBER: After succeeding for ten days with One Simple Rule, you will likely add additional rules to create a food plan that helps you achieve your ideal weight and other long-term goals. *I will help you do that later in this workbook. <u>So, as you go through and once again answer the below, assume you will see a dramatic difference in at least some areas after one full year of success</u>.*

www.WorkbookExamples.com has several audio examples of this exercise. You'll find them under the "Big Why" section.

As compared to how you're feeling today, how CONFIDENT do you look and feel in the mirror AFTER ONE FULL YEAR OF SUCCESS? In what ways does this manifest? Perhaps your face looks less bloated. Maybe you're holding yourself differently. Perhaps you're smiling just a little more, or your eyes look clearer. Maybe it's just in your choice of what to wear. What's different? In your imagination, look carefully and detail the difference below. Remember to imagine the best possible (yet still believable) result.

Remember – this is one year in the future and you've been in full control of your eating for a year. Imagine the most outrageously amazing result you can possibly believe. Also, as you go along try to use big exciting words and specifics. Don't say "I feel more confident" say "My confidence is soaring and I know there's no stopping me!"

As compared to today, what changes in your PHYSICAL CONDITIONS do you imagine seeing in the mirror AFTER ONE FULL YEAR OF SUCCESS? Maybe digestion is much better. Maybe your skin is much clearer. Maybe you can see a lot less physical pain, agitation, or inflammation in your eyes and your face. Perhaps your joints ache a lot less, or not at all anymore. Perhaps your face looks a lot less bloated. Maybe you're holding yourself differently. What's different? In your imagination, look carefully and detail the difference below. Remember, we are always imagining the best possible *(yet still believable)* result. Use big exciting words and specifics. Don't just say "I look good", say "I look bloody amazing! I can't believe it's me! I'm so gorgeous and proud!"

As compared to today, what changes in your MENTAL FREEDOM do you imagine might begin to develop AFTER ONE FULL YEAR OF SUCCESS? What might it be like to be completely free from over-thinking about and/or constant obsession with food? *Detail what you might like to be thinking about instead in one year below*! Use big exciting words and specifics. Don't just say "I am free of the mental obsession", say "My mind is clear, focused, present, and purposeful. I am able to concentrate my mental energy on important things like my children, my job, and my friends. I can't believe it!" *(Best possible yet still believable result)*

As compared to today, what changes in your HEALTH CONCERNS do you imagine might begin to develop after ONE FULL YEAR of success? Are these concerns more or less completely gone? What's it like to be free from *(or freer from)* that anxiety? Use big exciting words and specifics. Don't just say "I can't even imagine having a heart attack now... I feel so healthy, fit, and strong!" *(Best possible yet still believable result)*

_____

_____

_____

_____

_____

_____

_____

_____

_____

_____

_____

_____

_____

_____

_____

_____

_____

_____

_____

_____

As compared to today, what changes in your ENERGY LEVEL do you imagine might begin to develop AFTER ONE FULL YEAR OF SUCCESS? Most people find themselves with a LOT more physical energy at this point. Use big exciting words. Don't just say "I have more energy", say "I have boundless energy and have become a real dynamo, doing thing I only dreams of before like _____, _____, and _____!" *Say what you'd like to be DOING with the added energy! (Best possible yet still believable result)*

_____
_____
_____
_____
_____
_____
_____
_____
_____
_____
_____
_____
_____
_____
_____
_____
_____
_____

As compared to today, what changes in your RELATIONSHIPS do you imagine might begin to develop AFTER ONE FULL YEAR OF SUCCESS? How are things different with colleagues, friends, peers, children, spouse, and family? This all extends to your entire SOCIAL LIFE too. In your imagination, look carefully and detail the difference below. BE SPECIFIC. Use specific names to remind you later of your imagination. Use big exciting words. Don't just say "I'm closer with my husband", say "I can't believe it, but Manny and I have been intimate again and I love it! And the best part is we constantly communicate about important things, resolve conflict, and have become so much closer — it's better than I ever dreamed!" *(Best possible yet still believable result)*

As compared to today, what changes in your CLOTHING CHOICES do you imagine might begin to develop AFTER ONE FULL YEAR OF SUCCESS? Many people find themselves more likely to choose attractive clothes and enjoying more freedom and options because of changes in both their body and their confidence. In your imagination, look carefully and detail the difference below. Which clothes do you already have hanging in your closet which you *would* wear if you felt more confident about your shape? What clothing might you wear if you dropped a size? Two sizes? Use big, exciting words! Don't just say "I'd wear that pair of jeans in the closet." Instead say "I'd wear that sexy pair of black jeans with the hole in the knee that constantly turns heads!" *(Best possible yet still believable result)*

As compared to today, what changes in your CAREER OR FINANCES do you imagine might begin to develop AFTER ONE FULL YEAR OF SUCCESS? Some people find themselves more likely to take action on financial and/or career projects given the additional energy and mental/physical confidence they develop. In your imagination, look carefully and detail the difference below. If you DO see a difference in your financial and/or career activities, try to QUANTIFY how much of a financial impact there might be? Be specific. Imagine one or two things we could do to improve your career and/or finances if you felt like you ruled the world—a feeling which often comes when you learn to control your Pig! Use big, exciting words! Don't say "I make $10,000 more per year", say "The $10,000 extra I make every year has taken the edge completely off our financial situation. I feel CALM about money for the first time in my life, and it's only going to get better! After ten years I will have earned $100,000 that I wouldn't have if I kept overeating – it's amazing!" *(Best possible yet still believable result)*

As compared to today, what changes in your EXERCISE, SPORTS PARTICIPATION, AND/OR PHYSICAL ACTIVITY LEVEL do you imagine might begin to develop AFTER ONE FULL YEAR OF SUCCESS? Some people don't wish to incorporate this into their lives, but if you do, look carefully at what you imagine might develop. Detail the difference below. Talk about why it's important too if it applies. Perhaps you might add a short workout session every day. Or maybe you'd start planning to participate in a sport you've always wanted to do. Remember, in one year you'll be in a completely different place with your confidence, so what might you start dreaming about? Use big, exciting words! Don't say "I'll go back to hiking with the kids again", say "I will hike Soldier's Dome with the kids on July 12th next year to celebrate. I can see myself and the kids with arms high in the air to celebrate our victorious ascent!" *(Best possible yet still believable result)*

CRITICALLY IMPORTANT:

TAKE A BREAK FOR ONE TO FOUR DAYS BEFORE MOVING ON!

(The above exercise used a lot of your creative energy and I want you to recover and let the results sink in before you do the next exercise please)

Exercise 2B) Imagine you are nearing the end of your life, many, many years from now. Your One Simple Rule snowballed in a positive direction and spawned a whole set of healthy behaviors which you followed for a lifetime. See the people gathered round you in your final moments, giving thanks for all you've done. You've lived an almost ideal life, all beginning with the adoption of your one rule. You became a different person.

Who, specifically, is around you and thanking you? *(Best possible yet still believable result)*

_____

_____

_____

_____

_____

_____

_____

_____

_____

What are they thanking you for? What did you do with your life after you relinquished your overeating and/or food obsession? Imagine your confidence skyrocketed after you caged your Pig. And armed with this confidence you knew you could do ANYTHING. What have you accomplished?

_____

_____

_____

_____

_____

_____

_____

_____

What else did you do which these people may not even know about? What else did you accomplish in your life after freeing yourself from overeating?

_____

_____

_____

_____

_____

_____

_____

_____

_____

_____

How does it feel, knowing you lived the balance of your life free from overeating and food obsession?

_____

_____

_____

_____

_____

_____

_____

_____

_____

_____

_____

_____

Exercise 2C) Go through the two previous exercises *(2A + 2B)* and circle, underline, and/or star the benefits which are most important to you. There's no limit to what you can mark, although if you're emphasizing more than half what you wrote down you may want to be a little more discriminating. The goal is to emphasize what's MOST motivating to you.

☐ YES, I HAVE DONE THIS EXERCISE!
(Check after completing.)

Exercise 2D) What happens if you do NOT change course? What happens if you allow your Pig to continue to dominate you, not just in 10 days or one year, but in five years? The goal here, even though it may feel unpleasant, is to construct a very detailed and specific picture of what the future may hold. A foreshadowing of things to come if you don't change.

See, your Pig wants you to believe that, as bad as things may be, they will likely stay the same. For this reason, it says, you might as well just start "tomorrow." After all, it reasons, things are not really that bad, and "we could get away with just one more food binge – yippee!!" But, just as the "ghost of Christmas future" scared Ebenezer Scrooge into changing by showing him a picture of what's coming down the road, so too can this vision of the future have a mighty impact on you. Things almost never stay the same when people keep overeating. They get worse. Often much worse.

Seeing this future in vivid detail is a very powerful motivator! *So answer the following questions in as much specific detail as you can*. REMEMBER: Following your One Specific Food Rule is likely to lead to a positive snowball of health and behavioral changes over the course of five years, whereas continuing as you are may lead to a negative snowball in the same manner. It's ok if you feel a little emotional and scared. It's even OK if you cry a bit during this exercise. Because it's better that you cry once now and fully understand what the Pig has in store for you so you can avoid this future.

This is an EXTREMELY powerful exercise and if you are tempted to skip it because you don't want to feel bad about yourself, think how badly you'll feel in 5 years if you continue down the road you are presently on. It's therefore MUCH better to feel this pain once in your imagination than it is to feel it in real life, day after day.

➔ **What will happen to your confidence? How, specifically, will this negatively impact your life?**

_____

_____

_____

_____

_____

_____

_____

_____

_____

➔ **What *specific* negative changes in your physical conditions will you experience? Be detailed please.**

_____

_____

_____

_____

_____

_____

_____

_____

_____

➜ **What about your mental freedom from food?** What negative changes in your level of obsession with food may occur? In how often you think about it? In how much of your thinking about food crowds out *specific* things which are important to you and would be better to think about?

_____

_____

_____

_____

_____

_____

_____

_____

What *specific* health concerns would be worse as compared to today? How much worse? And would you have any NEW health concerns that you don't have today?

_____

_____

_____

_____

_____

_____

_____

_____

➔ **How might your energy and/or fatigue level change for the worse?** What *specific* negative impact will that have on your life as compared to today?

_____

_____

_____

_____

_____

_____

_____

_____

_____

_____

➔ **How might your relationships suffer as compared today?** Include the *specific* negative impact on colleagues, friends, peers, children, spouse, and family.

_____

_____

_____

_____

_____

_____

_____

_____

_____

_____

_____

_____

→ **How might you need to dress differently as compared today?** Include the *specific* clothing choices you'd have to make and/or could no longer make.

_____

_____

_____

_____

_____

_____

_____

_____

_____

→ **How might your career and/or finances have been negatively impacted?** Look carefully and detail the difference below. If you DO see a difference in your financial and/or career activities, try to QUANTIFY how much of a financial impact there might be in five years if you don't change.

_____

_____

_____

_____

_____

_____

_____

_____

_____

➔ **What negative changes in your exercise, sports participation, and/or physical activity level do you see five years from now if you don't change course?**

_____

_____

_____

_____

_____

_____

_____

_____

Exercise 2E) Review exercise 2D above and circle, underline, star, or otherwise emphasize the negative impacts you most want to avoid. Again, we're trying to discern here what is most motivating for you. Re-write your motivators in priority order here. You may wish to collect them on a separate piece of paper and/or on your computer first. Write your motivators below. I've left you lots of space to do so, but please don't feel obligated to fill it. Some people are hyper-focused on just a few motivators, while others may have a dozen or more. There is no good or bad. Your motivators are your motivators! One important note however: Even though many of the motivations you'll find in the "Ghost of Christmas Future" exercise may be negative; we want to re-word them in the positive because they'll be MUCH more effective this way. For example, you might be frightened of having a heart attack and/or a stroke five years from now if you don't change. The way you'd write that in this section is "To be completely free from fear of heart attacks and strokes." See what I mean? OK, now please write your motivators *in priority order* below.

Exercise 2F) Your "Big Why." The goal of this exercise is to create a mini-essay *(between one half page and one full page long)* which encapsulates everything that will motivate you to stay on track indefinitely. You do this by reading and re-reading everything you wrote in the previous exercise above (2E) and massaging them into your essay statement or "Big Why."

Here's an example of my own Big Why: Yours can be much longer or shorter provided it includes all the benefits you touched on above in approximate priority order. It's important to use your own creativity to make it motivating for you. Your Big Why is your reason for complying with your Food Plan at all times, so you begin it with this reminder:

> "I comply with my Food Plan 100% at all times because I want to feel 100% confident in my health and put to bed ANY remaining concerns about having a heart attack, stroke, or cancer. I want lots of pure, clean energy to work, work out, hike, and accomplish amazing things with the remainder of my life! I want to feel lighter, stronger, and physically freer to move in the second half of my life than I did in the first. I want to feel as confident as possible in my handsome appearance, so I can walk in the world and wield maximum power as a strong, compassionate, independent man. I want to avoid being distracted by painful digestion and the associated fatigue. I want to be 100% free of guilt over what I've eaten at all times. I want to get better, deeper, cleaner sleep. I want to shift my pleasure-seeking activities into more yoga and time outside. And I want to be an extremely successful weight management author who helps other people eat clean and enjoy all the benefits above!"

Now it's your turn.

On the following page, please massage ALL the benefits you noted in Exercise 2E above into an essay statement. You may wish to work on a separate piece of paper and/or your computer before writing it down here, but when you're done please either re-write it (optimal) by hand in the space below, or else print out and tape a copy of your Big Why to this page so you'll always have everything in one place.

MY BIG WHY

_____

_____

_____

_____

_____

_____

_____

_____

_____

_____

_____

_____

_____

_____

_____

_____

_____

_____

Exercise 2G) Programming Your "Big Why" Into Your Brain!

The point of developing your Big Why in all the exercises above was NOT just to get you in touch with it one time! The point was to clearly articulate the future you want AND the future you're trying to avoid, so we could keep it front and center in your mind (and your heart) forever! We painted a vivid picture so you could activate the automatic goal-seeking mechanisms in your mind and move you consistently forward towards this goal, even if you make mistakes.

Therefore, what you need to do now is decide upon a mechanism for constantly programming your mind each day with your Big Why. Personally, I've recorded mine into an MP3, put some motivating music behind it, and put a recurring note on my to-do list which I can't check off until I've listened to it each morning. Some people just write it out on an index card or a piece of paper and carry it with them. Others paste it on their bathroom mirror.

If you DO use a to-do system, it's a good idea to include a daily note to remind you to review your Big Why.

Whatever you do, don't make the mistake of accepting a silent reading of your Big Why as sufficient. There seems to be something about saying and/or hearing it out loud which makes all the difference.

Below, please write how you will repeatedly expose yourself to your Big Why on a daily basis:

Then—*and this is very important*—take the steps necessary to set this up right now, while the exercise is fresh in your mind. If you need to print out your Big Why and paste it on your bathroom mirror, do it! Same goes for the entry in your daily reminders and/or recording it into an MP3 and putting it on your smartphone. Whatever you need to do to ensure this gets done, make it happen today!

NOTE: The Big Why is more like a vitamin supplement than an antibiotic. It's the daily repetition, day in and day out which makes it work. Though it WILL change your mood, any one day's reading doesn't do all that much. It's the cumulative impact we are after!

Chapter 3

Obliterating Old Excuses And Limiting Beliefs

The very moment you declare that you commit to One Simple Rule your Pig will begin Squealing and shrieking at the top of its lungs. *"You can't do possibly do that! You've failed a million times before, so you'll definitely fail again now. Why even bother, let's just binge on some yummy Slop right now!"* Or *"Go ahead, do your stupid rule. I may not be able to get you now, but eventually I'll get you. You'll see!"* Or any of about three dozen other ruthlessly aggressive half-truths.

You can think of your Pig's Squeals as limiting beliefs, and in this section, I'll show you how to eradicate and begin to replace them with a success identity. The sole reason you lack *belief* in your ability to permanently lose weight is because of a set of very specific, irrational "Pig" thoughts running around your head which falsely limit your confidence and suggest it's impossible to comply with your Food Plan when, in fact, the truth is just the opposite.

Never Binge Again is quickly headed towards a million readers in the next 12 months because it identifies a fundamental truth about our addictive brains — for all intents and purposes, they're comprised of two parts: (1) Our human selves, capable of love, long term strategizing and planning *(e.g. for weight loss)*, creativity, music, art, and working with others to form a cooperative society and; (2) the Reptilian Brain, responsibility for our most primitive drives — feast or famine, fight or flight, emergency action, etc. The Reptilian Brain only knows "eat, mate, or kill" but can unfortunately borrow our facility for language and disguise its motives as our own thoughts. Combine this with billions of dollars spent by industry to stimulate our feast response—to engineer hyperpalatable concentrations of starch, sugar, fat, oil, salt, and excitotoxins to hit our bliss point without the nutrition to make us feel satisfied, and package it in a way which makes the Reptilian Brain think it's necessary to survive—and you get addictive overeating in full force. As the old saying goes, "just hand over the chocolate and nobody gets hurt!" It's a recipe for disaster.

Fortunately, by recognizing and disempowering the specific language this part of our brain uses to talk us into breaking our best laid plans, we can intervene in the stimulus-response cycle and retake control.

In this section we'll first capture everything your Pig is immediately saying in response to your One Simple Rule. It's important to get these all out, to the best of your ability WITHOUT trying to solve them first, because by getting them all in black and white we begin to drain the Pig's destructive energy.

Then, you'll see if you can identify the lies and/or logical distortions in what your Pig is saying. Most Squeals contain an element of truth, that's why they are so alluring, but when you examine them in the light of day, they really don't hold water. I'll share with you virtually every form of irrational diet-breaking justification I and my Master Coaches have heard over the course of several years from coaching clients. As we go through each one, I'll point out the logical errors in detail, so you won't have to suffer the same fate. Disempowering this false logic should dramatically boost your confidence.

Reading *some* of these Squeals will make you think I'm reading your mind. In fact, it's unlikely you won't be able to find a detailed example mirrored herein for every Squeal your Pig presents right out of the gate. That's great news because we have also identified the logical distortions and lies within each of these Squeals—we've done the hard work for you! But I'm NOT reading your mind. It turns out that while myself and my trained coaches have collectively done thousands of sessions with hundreds of clients, there are only a few dozen arguments the Pig can throw at you! Go through them carefully and I'll bet you can't think of even one that's not listed here. Don't let this throw you. It's just human nature revealing itself, and I happen to be the guy at the helm hearing all the B.S. excuses our Reptilian Brains try to pull on us. I'm not psychic, just focused and determined. I haven't read your diary, I promise!

Exercise 3A) List everything your Pig says right out of the gate: Why can't, shouldn't, or won't you be able to follow your rule, according to your pig? As soon as you commit to your One Simple Rule your Pig is going to try to convince you that this is just one more pathetic attempt at control which you'll never be able to follow through on. That's OK, it's just the way our brains are set up. In order to retake your power and gain the control you crave; we first need to simply list out every last thing the Pig says. So please write down below all the reasons your Pig says you can't, shouldn't, or won't be able to follow your One Simple Rule 100% for ten days. *Remember: Don't solve these now. Just list them.* And list ALL the reasons you hear your Pig saying! Go ahead and do it below: *(NOTE - I've lettered them for you to make them easier to refer to later – you do NOT have to fill every line!)*

YOU CAN FIND AUDIO EXAMPLE SESSIONS OF GETTING ALL THESE REASONS OUT ON THE TABLE AT www.WorkbookExamples.com.

A.

B.

C.

D.

E.

F.

G.

H. _____

I. _____

J. _____

K. _____

L. _____

M. _____

N. _____

O. _____

P. _____

Q. _____

R. _____

S. _____

T. _____

U. _____

V. _____

W. _____

X. _____

Y. _____

Z. _____

Exercise 3B) Circle and Star → Circle the Squeals which bother you most above. Star the single most difficult Squeal—the one you, at this moment, might feel at a complete loss to ever overcome. Do it now please.

Exercise 3C) Disputing and Disempowering Your Pig's Squeals: Not only will we help you find the answers to the Squeals you've listed above, we'll show you just about everything hundreds of other people's Pigs have come up—all their reasons to not follow a particular Food Rule! And you'll see where the logical distortions, half-truths, and lies are in all these Squeals. Every Squeal is a "limiting belief", and all the Squeals combined are preventing you from knowing at the deepest level that you can not only get your eating under control, but also lose weight and keep it off permanently. Your Pig Squeals in order to get you to cultivate a failure identity and make binging and overeating progressively more likely. But in this section, we are going to work on eradicating all the specific limiting beliefs which have previously convinced you that you are powerless to fix the problem. That way you can cultivate a success identity. And it's a lot easier than you think!

IMPORTANT - PLACE A BOOKMARK ON THE PREVIOUS PAGE WHERE YOU'VE LISTED ALL YOUR "OUT OF THE GATE" PIG SQUEALS (EXERCISE 3A ABOVE). Even just earmarking that page will help – you are going to be turning back and forth to it periodically as you go through this exercise.

NOW, AS YOU READ THROUGH EACH OF THE COMMON SQUEALS BELOW:

→ **Place a checkmark next to the Squeal itself if it was already included in your list of "Out of the Gate Squeals" in Exercise 3A above.** Then (important) write the *Common Squeal Number* next to the line in Exercise 3A so you can always find the detailed disputation for each Out of the Gate Squeal. For example, if I'd listed "Let's just start again tomorrow" in line C of Exercise 3A, then I'd place a "1" next to the C line because "start again tomorrow" is Common Squeal #1, as you'll soon see below.

→ **Underline and circle the reasoning within the Common Squeal detailed explanation which exposes the half-truth and/or logical distortion your Pig is relying on.** Why is this Squeal a lie? You'll want this to "pop" later on if you need to reference it.

→ **If you find a Common Squeal which DOES seem alluring to you sometimes but was NOT in your list of "out of the gate" Squeals, add it to Exercise 3A and follow the same instructions above.**

ONE MORE THING AND IT'S VERY, VERY IMPORTANT: There's a good deal of reading to do in this section before you begin to customize things for yourself. That's because it's imperative you understand the form the most common excuses take, and the logical flaws with in them. Some people feel "antsy" to get through this section and mistakenly rush it...

That's not a very good idea because in many ways this is the MOST important section of the book! See, while *every* irrational excuse for breaking a Food Plan will definitely NOT apply to your situation, knowing the full spectrum of excuses you're likely to encounter in your Never Binge Again journey is extremely helpful. See, when you disempower the irrational excuses you're most vulnerable to now, your Reptilian Brain will start shifting to others you haven't encountered yet. This way we remove the element of surprise and make it infinitely more likely you can resist! So please, follow the instructions to the letter here, even if they do involve a little more reading than writing than you might expect in a workbook, OK?

OK! Ready? Let's go. I'll repeat the instructions within each common Squeal for your convenience.

COMMON PIG SQUEAL #1 – "LET'S JUST START AGAIN TOMORROW."

The "let's overeat today and start our diet again tomorrow" lie is perhaps the most common idea which causes the vast majority of people to think permanent weight loss is impossible. Variations include "One last time", "Today doesn't count because [insert reason here] – we'll start again in the morning", "You're getting really good at getting back on track before too much damage is done, so go ahead and binge today, it won't be so bad and we can get on the plan for real tomorrow," etc.

There are five reasons this line of reasoning is patently false. By studying them you can thoroughly disempower this awful belief before it manifests as a confidence-ruining psychological cancer.

→ First, science clearly demonstrates that if you DO binge today, it will be HARDER to ignore the cravings tomorrow. On the other hand, if you stay on your plan today it will be even easier to eat healthy tomorrow. Research into the neuroplasticity of our learning systems shows that we are always either reinforcing or extinguishing our food patterns, there is really no "staying still." So, the idea it will be "just as easy" to begin again tomorrow is patently false. If you're in a hole, stop digging!

→ Second, you can't eat tomorrow, you can only eat NOW, because when tomorrow comes, it will be now again! The purpose of the "start tomorrow" justification for breaking your diet is to deny this fundamental fact and focus on the future instead of the present moment in order to make overeating possible NOW. But when you realize the ONLY time you can put food in your mouth is the present, and that it's ALWAYS the present (*e.g. when to-*

morrow comes it will be the present again), then you'll know how to push this silly thought out of your head. If you never overeat now, you'll never overeat again because the future is an infinite string of nows. During absolutely every second it took you to read this paragraph it was NOW, and as a matter of fact, it still is! So, when the "let's start tomorrow" idea pops up in your head just say to yourself "I always use the present moment to be healthy" or "I never overeat now" and you'll be fine.

➔ Third, every bite counts, every last one! Your brain may be able to warp itself around the false notion that what you eat today doesn't count because you'll make up for it "tomorrow" *(which never comes),* but your body can't. Each and every bite you take either nourishes you or saps your health. Every wrong decision reinforces the addiction and every right one weakens it. Every bite counts. Every bite, no matter what no matter what no matter what!!

➔ Fourth, your word is sacred. Knowing you can keep a promise to yourself means everything. Being able to make a plan and stick to it is the foundation of self-mastery, which is what allows you to accomplish virtually everything else in your life. For this reason, "one bite" off your diet can ruin your belief in yourself and interfere with the rest of your life in more profound ways than most people realize. For this reason, it's important to keep your diet plan reasonable – don't try to accomplish too much or lose too much weight too quickly. Instead, focus on plans you can and will stick with, so you can build your confidence day by day into a positive snowball which lasts the rest of your life. You need to know you will do what you say you're going to do, it's really important.

➔ Finally, if you give the Reptilian Brain an inch off your diet you know it will take a mile. That's why one bite off your diet is too many, even though your Reptilian Brain says one thousand is not enough. Tomorrow never comes. Use the present moment to be healthy.

> INSTRUCTIONS: a) Place a checkmark next to the Common
> Squeal Title above if it was already included in your
> list of "Out of the Gate Squeals" in Exercise 3A above,
> then write this *Common Squeal Number* next to the line
> representing the Squeal in Exercise 3A. For example,
> this is Common Squeal #1 "start tomorrow." If you had
> listed "start tomorrow on line C of exercise 3A, you'd
> go back and place the #1 next to line C therein; (b)
> If this Squeal bothers you, please underline and circle
> the reasoning within the detailed explanation above that
> exposes the half-truth and/or logical distortion your

```
Pig relies on above. Why is this Squeal a lie? Take notes
in the margins if need be; (c) If you find a Common Squeal
which DOES seem alluring to you but was NOT in your list
of "out of the gate" Squeals, add it to Exercise 3A and
follow the same instructions above.
```

COMMON SQUEAL #2 – "SCREW IT, YOU ALREADY BLEW IT!"

While the "start again tomorrow" lie may be responsible for beginning more overeating binges than any other thought, the "screw it we already blew it" lie is likely the cause of more damage than any other because it can causes people to turn simple diet-slips into all-out food orgies. In turn, this utterly saps their confidence that it's possible to permanently lose weight. There are three ways to combat this.

First, remember that the impact of a food binge is always quantitative, and every moment is an opportunity for harm reduction: 5,000 extra calories does more damage than 2,000. 10,000 calories does more damage than 5,000, etc. Eating a whole pizza is better than eating two of them. Five cupcakes are better than fifteen!

Second, the idea that making a mistake compels us to compound and multiply that mistake is patently ridiculous. If you accidentally chip a tooth, are you compelled to go get a hammer and bang the rest of them out? If you slip and fall while you're hiking a mountain, are you obligated to roll down the hill the rest of the way to the bottom? If you accidentally touch a hot stove, do you immediately think "Well, now I have to do that a whole bunch more times?" Of course not!

Third, remember that "if you're not perfect then you're nothing" is your Reptilian Brain's favorite lie. If you make a mistake you're not supposed to say "Oh my God I'm just pathetic. Obviously, I can't resist anything at all!" Instead, you're supposed to figure out what went wrong and use it to decide how to make corrections to your course, if any. Then you need to collect evidence of success. Maybe the binge lasted for fewer hours? You ate half the cake instead of the whole thing? How did that happen? How can you leverage that learning next time? Collecting small successes causes you to gradually build a success identity, which builds your confidence and makes it possible for you to stay on your diet longer. Finally, you're supposed to forgive yourself and aim at the bulls eye again. The way our neurology is set up we have to get better if we keep aiming at a target, examining why we hit and/or missed it, by how much, in what direction, etc.

Fourth, think of what successful people you admire might do in that situation. For example, when Hussein Bolt trips and falls while he is practicing for a race, he doesn't have a tantrum and start throwing his shoes everywhere, does he?

Finally, remember "past performance is no guarantee of future gain." Your Reptilian Brain does NOT have a time machine can't possibly know what you will eat tomorrow. But YOU can know what you'll eat NOW. And since the ONLY time you can put food in your mouth is the present, and it's ALWAYS the present, if you never break your diet NOW then you'll never break your diet. Even if you broke it 5 minutes or 5 hours ago, once you stop breaking your diet NOW, you've won!

As with confidence-sapping thought #1 just say to yourself "I always use the present moment to be healthy" or "I never overeat now" and you'll be fine.

> INSTRUCTIONS: a) Place a checkmark next to the Common Squeal Title above if it was already included in your list of "Out of the Gate Squeals" in Exercise 3A above, then write this *Common Squeal Number* next to the line representing the Squeal in Exercise 3A. (b) If this Squeal bothers you, please underline and circle the reasoning within the detailed explanation above that exposes the half-truth and/or logical distortion your Pig relies on above. Why is this Squeal a lie? Take notes in the margins if need be; (c) If you find a Common Squeal which DOES seem alluring to you but was NOT in your list of "out of the gate" Squeals, add it to Exercise 3A and follow the same instructions above.

COMMON SQUEAL #3 – "YOU'VE TRIED SO MANY TIMES BEFORE AND FAILED AT DIETING, THEREFORE YOU MUST INEVITABLY FAIL THIS TIME TOO!"

The "You've failed before so you must fail again" idea come in several alternate forms. You may hear your Reptilian Brain throw any of the following at you: "You'll just gain all the weight back again *(and more)*", "You're just a fat person and you'll break your stupid diet eventually, so why not give up now and be happy with that already!", "You've been doing this for X years and have already spent Y dollars trying Z diet programs, so why om earth will this time be any different?"

The idea you've always failed in the past so you must always fail in the future fools most dieters into believing permanent progress is impossible, but it's an easy idea to beat when you know how!

First, recognize that negative self-talk about mistakes is binge motivated! The Reptilian Brain's whole purpose in beating you down about your past failures is to make you feel too weak to resist overeating TODAY. It's very difficult to keep overeating if you refuse to keep criticizing yourself for past mistakes. Stop yelling at yourself and you'll find there's a LOT less to fuel the binges!

Second, remind yourself continuing to get up and try again is a sign of strength, not weakness! Your Reptilian brain therefore only thinks it's putting you down with this idea when it's actually complimenting you! How many of the world's most significant accomplishments were made by people who got it right on the first try? *Even if you've repeatedly fallen down for years, continuing to get up until you succeed is a mark of strength, not weakness!* People who keep getting up and trying to lose weight eventually find a way to lose it and keep it off. The Japanese have a proverb "Fall down seven times, get up eight." Furthermore, research suggests one of the primary distinctions between long-term weight loss and yo-yo dieting is simply the sheer number of attempts. More permanent weight loss is more often achieved by people who've tried and failed more often. The name of the game clearly IS staying in the game until you win the game!

Third, train yourself to collect evidence of success, not evidence of failure: We can choose which lens we use to gather evidence about our lives and experiences, and perhaps the biggest choice you'll ever make is whether to utilize the lens of success vs. the lens of failure. Your Reptilian Brain wants you to choose the lens of failure so you can build a failure identity and keep binging, but YOU want to use the lens of success and build a success identity. Make a habit of writing down what you did RIGHT each week with food, no matter what you did wrong! *(NOTE: Chapter 10 focuses on this and contains more detailed instructions and templates to get you going on this very important habit!)*

Fourth, remember that even if you've driven on a highway for one thousand miles without taking any exit, you can STILL take the very next one! There is *nothing* which compels you to stay on a highway which is taking you in a direction you don't want to go!

```
INSTRUCTIONS: a) Place a checkmark next to the Common
Squeal Title above if it was already included in your
list of "Out of the Gate Squeals" in Exercise 3A above,
then write this Common Squeal Number next to the line
```

representing the Squeal in Exercise 3A.(b) If this Squeal bothers you, please underline and circle the reasoning within the detailed explanation above that exposes the half-truth and/or logical distortion your Pig relies on above. Why is this Squeal a lie? Take notes in the margins if need be; (c) If you find a Common Squeal which DOES seem alluring to you but was NOT in your list of "out of the gate" Squeals, add it to Exercise 3A and follow the same instructions above.

COMMON SQUEAL #4 – OK, I CAN'T GET YOU NOW BUT I'LL GET YOU LATER

In addition to confidence sapping thought #3, there are a variety of ways your Reptilian Brain will try to predict the future as if it had a time machine: *"I can't get you now but I'll get you later"*, *"You're going to forget your plan and then I'll get you"*, *"It only takes one time when you're too weak and/or not paying attention and then I'll get you!"*

In all of these ridiculous ideas the answer is the same: Your Reptilian Brain does not have a time machine and can't see the future any better than you can. Moreover, it's only *pretending* to be attacking you in the future! Really, it's trying to make you feel hopeless in the *present,* so you'll choose to break your diet NOW. You therefore only need remember to use the present moment to be healthy and never overeat now, because it will always be now! *(All you need to do is push the Pig's thoughts out of your head NOW – the future doesn't matter.)*

Also, remember that the nature of a commitment is a plan to remember, whereas your Reptilian Brain wants you to make a plan to forget. We regularly expect people to commit 100% to remembering their promises. For example, I've never heard the following vow at a wedding *"I really want to promise to be faithful and not sleep with any other women for the rest of our lives… but there sure are a lot of attractive people out there. What if I forget?"*

It's highly unlikely you'd accept this vow from your fiancé, so why accept the "what if I forget" excuse from your own Reptilian Brain?

It can also be helpful to think of every rule on your diet as being preceded by the words "Consciously and purposefully." For example, if I have a rule on my diet which says "I will never have chocolate during the week", but then happen to be at a Mexican Restaurant on a Wednesday evening, only to realize after talking to the waiter that my spicy dish actually had a little chocolate in it, I would NOT consider this a break… up to the point the waiter informed me I'd just eaten a little chocolate… because I didn't consciously and purposefully set out to eat it. However, if I took even one more bite with full knowledge of what I was doing, then I WOULD consider it a break indeed.

The 'consciously and purposefully' clause helps protect you from the Reptilian Brain saying "Well, you accidentally broke your diet so now the 'screw it you already blew it' plan is in effect, at least until tomorrow, so we can binge all day today!" The astute reader will realize this is *also* a ridiculous idea to be ignored as we've gone over previously, but the 'consciously and purposefully' clause saves you the mental work of having to go through this and can therefore be helpful at times.

```
INSTRUCTIONS: a) Place a checkmark next to the Common
Squeal Title above if it was already included in your
list of "Out of the Gate Squeals" in Exercise 3A above,
then write this Common Squeal Number next to the line
representing the Squeal in Exercise 3A.(b) If this Squeal
bothers you, please underline and circle the reasoning
within the detailed explanation above that exposes the
half-truth and/or logical distortion your Pig relies
on above. Why is this Squeal a lie? Take notes in the
margins if need be; (c) If you find a Common Squeal which
DOES seem alluring to you but was NOT in your list of
"out of the gate" Squeals, add it to Exercise 3A and
follow the same instructions above.
```

COMMON SQUEAL #5 – DIETING IS TOO HARD – YOU'LL BE TORTURED WITH INTOLERABLE CRAVINGS FOR WAY TOO LONG!

There are a number of reasons why the idea that dieting will feel too depriving can be false. First, recall that people who successfully keep the weight off after losing it developed an intrinsic type of motivation which turned them into a different kind of person with regards to food. Successful weight loss people actually don't see themselves as dieters at all. Instead, they enjoy the process and the journey of changing their eating identity. They also generally don't try to lose weight quickly, settling instead for an extremely reliable, consistent, and persistent pound or two per week. *(I believe there's an evolutionary mechanism in the brain which says "if nutrition and/or calories are too scarce for too long a period of time, then the moment they are available we had better hoard them!" Therefore, when people try to lose weight too quickly, they become prone to stimulating a harsh rebound where they find themselves overeating more than they'd ever done before. The solution is to take yourself OUT of feast and famine mode and keep a regular, reliable course of nutrition running through your body each day. Create a small caloric deficit when you want to lose weight. Either discuss this with a licensed dietitian to create a plan for losing a pound or two per week, or else consider using one of the online nutritional calculators like Cronometer.com or MyFitnessPal.com.)*

So, the initial answer is that dieting is only torturous when we MAKE it torturous. Lose weight slowly and it can be a lot more comfortable.

But there are two more answers to the "you'll feel way too deprived" lie...

The first one has to do with the neurological principles of downregulation and upregulation. See, your cravings will NOT last forever, even though your Reptilian Brain says you'll be indefinitely tortured by them. Let me explain.

When I was in graduate school, I had an apartment almost right beneath an elevated subway line in New York City. The first week I was there the trains were so loud I couldn't sleep at all! But you know what? A few weeks later I could barely hear them at all anymore and I slept like a baby. It turns out our nervous system "down-regulates" its response to a super-sized stimulus like the subway noise. Similarly, if you eat a chocolate bar every day your body will down-regulate its response to this unnaturally concentrated form of sweet, fat, and central nervous system stimulation. As a consequence, the natural sugars in fruit and vegetables just won't taste sweet anymore. In fact, this can get so bad that some people feel they need candy (the supersized stimulus) just to "feel normal." But the opposite is also true. Move away from the subway and you'll start to be more sensitive to loud noises again within a matter of weeks. Stop eating sugar and your taste buds should regenerate and double in sensitivity in the same time frame.

So, the Reptilian Brain tells you that you'll be tortured forever without its favorite junk, but it's LYING, I promise! When I stopped eating chocolate to lose weight, I stopped having cravings after only a few months. The very same thing happened to me with flour. It took about 8 weeks for 80% of the cravings to go away, then at the six months mark I'd say they were 80% diminished again (maybe 5% of what they once were).

Unfortunately, this extinction curve *(wherein cravings can diminish roughly according to the schedule I described)* gets reset every time you indulge. It turns out we are almost always either downregulating or upregulating, there's virtually no in-between. So the truth is that if cravings are bothering you what you want to do is STAY on your plan! That way you stimulate the upregulation process and you begin to find more pleasure from healthier foods.

The final answer to the "you'll be too deprived" lie is that you're actually depriving yourself more by continuing to indulge than by changing your habits.

See, unbeknownst to most people, there are TWO ways to be deprived: (1) There is depriving yourself of pleasure by NOT having something and; (2) there's what you deprive yourself of by having it. *(First articulated by Geneen Roth.)*

It's rare for people to choose between these two alternatives because they generally never consider the second kind at all.

Just for illustration, and please know I'm NOT suggesting you adopt this rule, let's take the notion of never eating donuts again. If you never eat donuts again, you'll deprive yourself of the taste, texture, and mouth feel of donuts for the rest of your natural life. You will never experience donut pleasure again. To a donut -loving Reptilian Brain, this is a fate worse than death!

But...

If you *continue* eating donuts, you will deprive yourself of everything associated with *never* eating donuts again including (a) obtaining the body of your dreams *(or something close);* (b) the "lightness of spiritual being" found in a life without all that extra weight; (c) the energy associated with more regular, healthy nourishment *(assuming you replace the chocolate with something healthy);* (d) knowing what it's like to have consistent blood sugar levels and to live without sugar crashes; (e) the *confidence* which comes from knowing you have the power to NEVER eat donuts again; (f) years near the end of your life which were meant to be pain-free and full of joy, but are instead filled with immobility and dysfunction due to strokes, heart attacks, etc.

Your Reptilian Brain wants you to concentrate only on the *short-term* effects of donut deprivation because it genuinely believes donuts are the *only* pleasure life has to offer. But the list of things we deprive ourselves of by *continuing* a destructive food behavior is often a LOT longer and more painful!

To take advantage of this insight you only need to make a solid comparison between your two choices. What will you deprive yourself of if you continue to embrace the food *(or behavior)* vs. letting it go?

And I'll tell you what, let's give your Reptilian Brain a running start by letting it go first. Think about some treat you *just might* want to consider avoiding from now on. Go ahead and tell your Reptilian brain to provide you with a long list of things you'll be depriving yourself of if you *never* eat it again.

Can you feel your Reptilian Brain squirming? That's because there are only two things it can really posit in this situation—taste and convenience. Oh, it will SAY you'll be depriving yourself of life itself—*that you'll starve to death in a matter of hours without its junk.* But by now your Reptilian Brain knows you're on to *that* game, so the best it can do is say "because it tastes good" or "it's so easy to just grab it and go." It squirms at this exercise because it knows its ammunition pales in comparison to your side of the equation.

Take control and write down your list. *(Hint – you've already done it in your Big Why – exercise 2E. You lose the opportunity to experience the things in your Big Why if you keep overeating.)* Make yourself immune to the deprivation lie!

Let your Reptilian Brain say as much as it wants to about how deprived you'll feel when you stop eating its junk. When you write these things down it should become clear to you that your Reptilian Brain is talking about itself. It will feel deprived, not you!

Then write down everything you can think of which YOU will be deprived of by keeping the junk in your diet.

See, a well-considered, informed decision between the two types of deprivation always favors you, no matter the specifics of the diet rule under consideration. So just write down the facts and make your choices.

Alternative forms of the "you'll be too deprived" confidence sapping lie are ""You simply can't give up that much pleasure", "Food is your only real pleasure in life and you'll suffer too much without unlimited access to whatever you want", "I'll make your life unbearable forever by constantly asking for more", etc.

> INSTRUCTIONS: a) Place a checkmark next to the Common Squeal Title above if it was already included in your list of "Out of the Gate Squeals" in Exercise 3A above, then write this *Common Squeal Number* next to the line representing the Squeal in Exercise 3A. (b) If this Squeal bothers you, please underline and circle the reasoning within the detailed explanation above that exposes the half-truth and/or logical distortion your Pig relies on above. Why is this Squeal a lie? Take notes in the margins if need be; (c) If you find a Common Squeal which DOES seem alluring to you but was NOT in your list of "out of the gate" Squeals, add it to Exercise 3A and follow the same instructions above.

COMMON SQUEAL #6 – NO PARTICULAR DIET WILL EVER BE GOOD ENOUGH SO LET'S JUST KEEP JUMPING FROM DIET TO DIET!

This is the belief and confidence destroying experience of having been convinced to try diet after diet, forever jumping from one to the next, never giving any one of them enough time and serious commitment to see if it works. Alternatively, we call this the "Grass is Greener on the Other Side" lie, or the "Confused and Conquer" strategy of your Reptilian Brain.

The way to beat this lie is to remember it's usually better to solidly try a reasonable diet plan for a month than to jump from plan to plan. This is true even if the plan you're working with is clearly flawed in some way. It's better to have SOME rules in place than to allow chaos to reign free, because in the absence of rules your Reptilian Brain will have a field day and all bets are off!

The grass is NOT greener on the other side, the grass is greener where it's watered.

Another way to beat this lie is to require yourself to have a minimum of 72 hours before you allow yourself to change your dietary rules. This way you can't ever do so impulsively based upon the whims of the Reptilian Brain.

> INSTRUCTIONS: a) Place a checkmark next to the Common Squeal Title above if it was already included in your list of "Out of the Gate Squeals" in Exercise 3A above, then write this *Common Squeal Number* next to the line representing the Squeal in Exercise 3A.(b) If this Squeal bothers you, please underline and circle the reasoning within the detailed explanation above that exposes the half-truth and/or logical distortion your Pig relies on above. Why is this Squeal a lie? Take notes in the margins if need be; (c) If you find a Common Squeal which DOES seem alluring to you but was NOT in your list of "out of the gate" Squeals, add it to Exercise 3A and follow the same instructions above.

COMMON SQUEAL #7 – "YOU'RE GOING TO LET ME OUT ON PURPOSE."

This is actually an alternate form of the "I can't get you now, but I'll get you later" lie. So, you CAN address it in exactly the same way, remembering that later doesn't matter because the future is an infinite string of "nows", and the only time you can eat is now. So, if you always use the present to be healthy, then your Reptilian Brain can prognosticate all it likes about you deciding to let it out on purpose later, but later will be now again.

That said, when people consistently relate that they recognized their Reptilian Brain craving its junk, but then consciously and purposefully decided to feed it, only to feel horrendously regretful afterwards, there are often precipitating facts which can easily be addressed. You CAN beat this pattern.

First, double check to ensure you REALLY have a nutritionally sufficient and balanced diet. All the techniques in the world won't help if you're not consuming enough calories and nutrients on a regular, day to day basis. If the body is deprived of sustenance, it will eventually sense a pending 'starvation' period, and "force" you to be less discriminating about food. *There are SOME rules humans can NEVER stick to no matter how good they are at NBA.* For example, you could NEVER indefinitely stick to a rule which says "I Will Never Pee Again"... you just can't! This is step one, and without it, there is no step two.

Second, adopt the belief that there's ALWAYS a reason to be found which justified the dietary transgression, despite the perception that you "just did it" or "went unconscious and did it automatically." See, your Reptilian Brain much prefers you don't become aware of the reason you used to justify crossing the line again, because if there really were NO reason, then the Reptilian Brain could get you to feed it whenever it wanted some junk... "just cause."

So what you want to do is dig deep into everything which preceded the first bite of the mistake and try to remember exactly what happened. Reconstruct exactly what you ate, when you ate it, what you were thinking/feeling/doing in the hours leading up to the mistake, what happened before you heard the "screw it let's do it" lie, what specific thoughts and feelings sustained the overeating episode, or what people and places sustained it *(where did you buy the junk, who from, how did you hide it from others, etc.),* how and when did you decide to stop.

By going through this analysis in detail you'll accomplish two very important things: (1) You'll convince yourself there were literally a dozen or more decision points where you could've intervened and decided NOT to indulge, thereby increasing your ability to make the right choice next time; (2) You'll become more confident that your Reptilian Brain can't just "knock you unconscious" and "make" you break your diet as an automated action.

Dig deep for lack of self-care, feelings of overwhelm, and blood sugar management problems during the time leading up to the conscious food mistake, then problem solve these to make a plan for preventing them next time.

On its surface the reason for the mistake may seem trivial or silly *(e.g. "Screw it, let's do it!")*... in reality once you've gone through the above though, you'll be able to pin-point the specific rationalization (lie) and circumstances which justified the mistake, which will give you a LOT more confidence that you don't have to let it happen again.

Finally, remind yourself that if you can CHOOSE to eat something off your diet, you can choose to stick to your diet too! The mistake itself is evidence of your free will, and you have a choice regarding how to use it in the future.

Oh, one last thing, and it's important! While the retrospection process above is very helpful, the key to solving the 'unconscious eating' problem is to practice the skill of calling out your Pig. Get into the habit of asking your Pig "Oh yeah? Why in the world should I even consider eating this?" *whenever* you are entertaining the thought of eating something outside of your Food Plan! And FORCE your Pig to answer! You'll find you can then win the battle the vast majority of the time.

```
INSTRUCTIONS: a) Place a checkmark next to the Common
Squeal Title above if it was already included in your
list of "Out of the Gate Squeals" in Exercise 3A above,
then write this Common Squeal Number next to the line
representing the Squeal in Exercise 3A. (b) If this Squeal
bothers you, please underline and circle the reasoning
within the detailed explanation above that exposes the
half-truth and/or logical distortion your Pig relies
on above. Why is this Squeal a lie? Take notes in the
margins if need be; (c) If you find a Common Squeal which
DOES seem alluring to you but was NOT in your list of
"out of the gate" Squeals, add it to Exercise 3A and
follow the same instructions above.
```

COMMON SQUEAL #8 – "YOU'RE NOT LOSING WEIGHT FAST ENOUGH!"

People who struggle with overeating are often also expert dieters, stuck in the "feast and famine" cycle. Generally, they go through phases of overeating until they are fed up with the weight, bloating, fatigue, and difficulty choosing clothing... then they plunge headlong into a diet to lose the weight. Generally the dieting becomes less effective over time, and they unfortunately also tend to gain more weight back during the next overeating phase than they lost in the dieting phase. This results in the all-too-familiar creeping up of weight as the years go by.

The problem with losing weight too quickly is that it seems to signal the brain that we are in an environment where food, calories, and nutrition are scarce. Then, the moment we give in and overeat, we signal it that "the harvest is here" and we plunge into a "food hoarding" mode... taking in as many calories as we can.

This is a BAD roller coaster to ride for all the above reasons and more. Your Reptilian Brain knows this and endeavors to keep you riding it by encouraging you to try and lose weight fast, however, because it knows when you do, the roller coaster will almost inevitably swing the other way and it will get to have another serious overeating period.

The best solutions I've found with literally hundreds of clients is to create a reliable, consistent-but-small caloric deficit which results in a weight loss of perhaps one or two pounds per week, maximum. I personally knew a man *(let's call him Joe)* who lost *hundreds* of pounds at the rate of only 5 pounds per month. When I asked him how he put himself in the right mindset, he said he'd come to the conclusion that the FASTEST way to lose the weight was SLOWLY, because his years of radical dieting and weight loss had only led him to 500+ pounds. "I did the crime, so I've gotta do the time" he said. "I used to do my best to cheat the system and 'break out' of the 'fat prison' I made for myself, but now I know the door is wide open if I can just take one *small* step every month."

Here are a few extremely helpful things you can do if you've got a lot of weight to lose and your Reptilian Brain has you convinced you're not losing it fast enough:

➔ Remind yourself direction is much more important than speed. The philosopher Socrates is said to have been asked by a young traveler how to get to Mt. Olympus. "That's easy", said Socrates, "Just be sure every step you take is in the direction of Mt. Olympus." You got to where you are because every step you took was NOT in the direction of your goal, but if you simply pay attention and ensure that your steps are moving you towards it, you'll get there! *(Thanks to Doug Graham, author of the "80 10 10 Diet" for the "Direction is more important than speed" mantra.)*

➔ Reframe the problem. It's overwhelming to think of having to lose 100 pounds, so instead, set out to lose ONE pound, one hundred times!

➔ Calculate a realistic date for when you'll get to goal weight, as well as several significant milestones all along the way. If you can stick to a five pound per month plan, where will you be in three months? Six months? Then ask yourself how you'll feel in one month, three months, six months, and one year. How will it feel, for example, to be thirty pounds lighter in six months? Sixty pounds lighter this time next year? If that's really not sufficient for you, use an eight pound per month fat-loss rate, but never more than this please. *(Eight pounds per month is almost one hundred pounds per year).*

➜ Remind yourself "the fastest way to lose weight is slowly", like Joe did above. I've definitely seen the most long-term success on a slow and steady weight loss plan. I've also seen MOST people bounce back to where there were before (and worse) when they lose weight too quickly. And remember, I've worked with hundreds of people on weight loss!

➜ Remember that there are sometimes plateaus as you are losing weight and your set point is adjusting. Sometimes too your diet may need adjusting. The only way you can do this rationally is by sticking to it. Your Reptilian Brain will try to confuse the issue and say your current plan isn't working when it's actually the overeating episodes—*the times you do NOT stick to the diet, NOT the diet itself*—which is sabotaging your progress!

IMPORTANT EXCEPTION: If your doctor requires you to lose weight more quickly for any reason please override my advice above. I'm not a medical doctor and haven't performed a physical exam on you, so please listen to your doctor.

> INSTRUCTIONS: a) Place a checkmark next to the Common Squeal Title above if it was already included in your list of "Out of the Gate Squeals" in Exercise 3A above, then write this *Common Squeal Number* next to the line representing the Squeal in Exercise 3A. (b) If this Squeal bothers you, please underline and circle the reasoning within the detailed explanation above that exposes the half-truth and/or logical distortion your Pig relies on above. Why is this Squeal a lie? Take notes in the margins if need be; (c) If you find a Common Squeal which DOES seem alluring to you but was NOT in your list of "out of the gate" Squeals, add it to Exercise 3A and follow the same instructions above.

COMMON SQUEAL #9 – "YOU'LL BE TOO STRESSED AND/OR OVERWHELMED BY YOUR EMOTIONS IF YOU DON'T EAT A LOT OF 'COMFORT FOOD' SO YOU'LL EVENTUALLY BREAK NO MATTER WHAT!"

The idea you 'need' to overeat in order to deal with your emotions is one of the most common misconceptions in the modern world. Alternative forms of this lie generally include specific emotions to fear: Anger, loneliness, excitement, sadness, and anxiety.

If you eat for emotional reasons, you should know that the relationship between overeating and emotional upset is more complex than you may think—I studied it for decades, even funding my own 40,000-person online study during the years I was binge eating and trying to figure it out! In that study I DID discover an interesting link between types of food people overate and the specific emotional problems they reported. For example:

→ People who struggled with chocolate were more likely to report feeling lonely, broken-hearted, or depressed...

→ People who overate salty, crunchy snacks were more often stressed at work...

→ People who binged on pasta and bread tended to be upset with their life at home...

Not everyone fit into these findings, but they were significant.

Personally, I've always had a chocolate problem, so those findings were particularly intriguing to me. I therefore looked into my own heart. Yes, I was in a bad marriage and feeling heartbroken, but I wanted to know more about how this pattern—Glenn feels compelled to overeat chocolate whenever he's upset—began. What was the 'root' of the problem?

My mother also happens to have been a psychotherapist, so I asked her for insight into what might have happened in my youth that might be relevant. Here's what she said, with a big embarrassed look on her face:

> "Glenn, when you were only one year old in 1965 your Dad was a captain in the army. I was awfully scared they were going to send him to Viet Nam. Your grandpa had also been missing for 9 months, and when he emerged, I found out he'd been in jail for fraud... and he was guilty! This was absolutely devastating because I'd always adored him – he was the only real saving grace in the very difficult childhood you know I had. So, there I was, depressed, anxious, and overwhelmed on so many levels. And there YOU were, needing love, attention, and healthy food, but I didn't have it in me to give it to you. At least not all the time. You DESERVED hugs and love and attention and healthy food, but I just couldn't provide it. More often I was just sitting and staring at the wall, feeling extremely overwhelmed, anxious, and depressed. So, when you came crying to me, I'd just

> *give you some Bosco chocolate syrup and that would calm you down. Eventually I put it in a refrigerator on the floor so you could go get it yourself. You'd go grab the bottle, suck down some chocolate sugar syrup, and go into a 'food coma' for an hour or so."*

Now, this was a very good conversation to have. It helped me feel more compassion for my mother's struggles. She did indeed have a very hard life. It also helped me feel more compassion for myself – there was a REASON I felt compelled to eat chocolate when I got upset. I could forgive myself and stop hating myself for this trouble. But it did NOT improve my relationship with chocolate. In fact, I got worse and started eating more...

I now know that was because emotional insight improves your life but does not cure over-eating! As long as you think you must overcome all your emotional issues in order to stop overeating, and as long as you think you're only eating for 'comfort' you'll just be giving your Reptilian Brain one more excuse to keep overeating.

Here's the thing...

Your emotional issues may have lit the match that started the fire but once it's burning, that fire takes on a life of its own. See, the hyper-palatable, industrial food-like-substances people typically binge on *(bags, boxes, bars, containers, etc.)* are NOT natural. These things did not exist in the tropics while we were evolving, and we have NOT been physically prepared to deal with the immensely pleasurable sensations they produce. In essence, once the fire's been started there is an intense craving which gets programmed right into your personal neurology...

A DESIRE TO "GET HIGH" WITH FOOD WHICH EXISTS INDEPENDENT OF ANY EMOTIONAL CONFLICT YOU MAY BE EXPERIENCING! *(Read that again, it's important.)*

What you need to do most urgently is PUT OUT THE FIRE, not dive into a deep investigation to figure out what started it. You CAN investigate later on to improve your life in other ways, but for God's sake don't get stuck in years of emotional analysis trying to find the burnt match while the fire is devouring your home!

As far as overeating is concerned, it's much more important to be a fireman than a detective.

Thankfully, there's a simple way to do this:

First, don't tell yourself you're overeating for emotional reasons, to relieve stress, to "cope", or to comfort yourself. That's a mindset which feeds the fire and gives your Reptilian Brain an excuse. *("We're WAY too upset. These feelings are awful. We MUST go get comfort food to escape them!" – Your Reptilian Brain)*

Then, remind yourself you're binging to get high with food, much like a drug addict might do with drugs. This makes it more uncomfortable to you to keep doing it and takes away your Reptilian Brain's favorite excuse...a GOOD thing!

Decide you're willing to go through ANY level of emotional discomfort in order to remain on your diet. Although this new attitude may feel very uncomfortable at times, you won't continue to distract yourself and/or waste your valuable physical and mental energy on recovering from overeating. This energy then becomes more available to SOLVE the problems you're facing. "The only way out is through."

Remember that if you've got six problems and then you overeat, well, then you'll have seven problems.

To elaborate, let's say you're stressed out about money problems and you binge. You'll get maybe an hour of relief from your money problems while the high from the Slop lasts, max. But after that hour you'll still be stressed about money problems AND you'll feel bloated and self-conscious from all the Slop going through your body. You'll probably also sleep badly and wake up cranky. So, starting off you were stressed out about money, but post binge you're *still* stressed out about money, but now you're also feeling ashamed, guilty, bloated, and tired.

That's not what you wanted to achieve, is it?

But if you resist the need to binge, then you'll feel more confident, more in control, have more energy and then you'll be able to cope and maybe even begin to solve your money issues. Now, that's better!

Accept that fact that you do NOT have to get rid of emotions *(or fix the problems they represent)* before you can stop overeating. In fact, the opposite is true. One must let their Reptilian Brains know they're willing to feel any degree of emotional discomfort while STILL sticking to your diet.

I distinctly remember having to implement the above insight the week my Mom got the recurrence of ovarian cancer which killed her 3 months later. That same week I also learned a dear friend had unexpectedly died in his sleep. And I had another rather serious personal struggle with a woman I was dating at the time.

See, life unfortunately isn't a pain-free experience. Happiness is not guaranteed just because we stop overeating. What you get when you eliminate overeating from your life is LIFE - for better or for worse. *Marry your life, not your Reptilian Brain*. It's much better to be present no matter what emotional pain life brings than to spend days, weeks, or months recovering from overeating.

Once you REALLY understand all this, you'll stop letting emotions confuse the issue. Oh, you'll still have them, perhaps even more so, but you'll understand they don't run the show. You've simply been lying down, drowning in six inches of mud this whole time, when all you ever needed to do was stand up, wash off the muck, and walk away.

It took me three decades to get this. I'll never get those utterly wasted 30 years back, and I'd like to save you this pain. From the bottom of my heart to the bottom of yours I know you CAN do this!

```
INSTRUCTIONS: a) Place a checkmark next to the Common
Squeal Title above if it was already included in your
list of "Out of the Gate Squeals" in Exercise 3A above,
then write this Common Squeal Number next to the line
representing the Squeal in Exercise 3A. (b) If this Squeal
bothers you, please underline and circle the reasoning
within the detailed explanation above that exposes the
half-truth and/or logical distortion your Pig relies
on above. Why is this Squeal a lie? Take notes in the
margins if need be; (c) If you find a Common Squeal which
DOES seem alluring to you but was NOT in your list of
"out of the gate" Squeals, add it to Exercise 3A and
follow the same instructions above.
```

COMMON SQUEAL #10 – "YOU CAN'T 100% COMMIT TO ANY DIET – THAT'S JUST A SET UP FOR GUILT AND SHAME WHEN YOU FAIL!"

In our culture we are commonly told that guidelines are better than rules. "Anything in moderation", "just eat healthy 90% of the time", "trying to make a hard and fast rule is just a form of restriction against which you'll eventually have to rebel, and then you'll beat yourself up with guilt and shame, making you want to overeat even more!", "strive for progress, not perfection", etc.

Would it surprise you to learn this is the wrong advice?

Here's the problem, as originally outlined in my book "45 Binge Trigger Busters": Guidelines require you to make constant decisions about whether or not to eat this or that...and the research suggests decisions wear down your willpower. It seems there are only so many good decisions we can make each day. Therefore, if you say "I'm going to avoid chocolate 90% of the time and eat it only 10% of the time," you've put yourself into a bad position, because you'll now have to make a chocolate decision every time you're at the checkout counter in Starbucks staring at a chocolate bar with your name on it. That burns a LOT of willpower!

In contrast, if you say "I'll only ever eat chocolate again on the last 3 days of the Calendar Month, and never more than 2 oz per day" you've accomplished the same 90/10 split because 3 days out of 30 is ten percent. Except this time the vast majority of your chocolate decisions are made for you already, and therefore vastly less willpower will be required to stick to your plan!

Ultimately the latter strategy is a character-building statement. You've articulated your intention to *become the kind of person* who eats chocolate only 3 days per month, and in so doing you'll have discovered a secret very few people know: *Character trumps willpower.*

Guidelines are also way too easy for our Reptilian Brains to break through. For example, if you say "I mostly avoid chocolate" and the Reptilian Brain has a strong craving, how do you know if TODAY is one of the days you avoid it or not? All it need do is say: "You DO avoid chocolate most of the time, so let's have some TODAY!" That's because the "most" in "most of the time" is ambiguously defined. Does it mean 92% of the time? 67% of the time? 51% of the time? Your guess is as good as mine. Or your Reptilian Brain's.

The REAL meaning of a guideline like "I avoid chocolate most of the time" really is "I'll try to avoid chocolate until I don't feel like avoiding it anymore." This might work for some naturally skinny people, or those who don't really like chocolate that much... but for those of us with a serious chocolate problem it's actually NO help at all. In fact, it makes things worse because it draws attention to chocolate without providing a solid protection against it.

Guidelines favor your Reptilian Brain, but *rules and well-defined diets* favor you!

See, "I'm only ever going to eat chocolate again on the last three days of the Calendar Month" is unassailable by your Reptilian Brain. Either today is one of the last three days of the month or it isn't. 10 observers could follow you around for a month and agree on whether you kept to the rule 100% or you didn't. The use of the word "never" in your rule means "under any circumstances whatsoever" and excludes ALL possible exceptions. The word "again" means "between now and the day the universe is no more" ...so your Reptilian Brain can't say "Oh, well, you didn't really mean you were going to do that *forever*, did you?"

Unfortunately, over-eaters tend to favor *guidelines* because they believe it's impossible to commit to anything 100% and forever. They fear excessive guilt and negative self-talk when and if they make a mistake. And since, as a practical matter most people DO make mistakes, they conclude "never" or "always" have NO place in their dietary rules...

This is blatantly incorrect, but it takes a little explanation to understand why. See, the fear of getting stuck with too much guilt after a mistake actually represents an erroneous understanding of the appropriate role for guilt in the psyche. Berating yourself for a mistake is the WRONG attitude. If you mess up, you're supposed to take a hard look at what went wrong and figure out how to do better next time, NOT repeatedly smack yourself in the head with a spatula! It's like touching a hot stove by accident. You WANT to feel pain in that situation so it gets your attention and you can figure out how to avoid it in the future, but you're NOT supposed to say "OMG, I'm a pathetic hot stove toucher, I might as well put my whole hand down on the grill!"

In fact, the self-punishment which occurs for many over-eaters after a serious food mistake is really their Reptilian Brains attempting to convince them they're too weak to hold to their diets... their Reptilian Brains are trying to get them to REPEAT the mistake! Once you understand this, it becomes a lot easier to let go of the guilt and shame and just move on.

Perfectionism is incorrect *when looking back on your mistakes*, but the right *(and only)* mindset to adopt *when looking forward towards your goals*. For example, if you wanted to climb a mountain peak, you should visualize yourself victoriously enjoying the view from the top. Purge ALL doubt and distraction about the possibility of failure from your mind so you can concentrate your energy on accomplishing your goal. That's what winner's do!

If it weren't possible to vow to do something forever, what justification could we possibly ever have for marriage? I've yet to hear the following vow at a wedding: *"I promise to love and be faithful...until an inevitable moment of weakness. I promise I'll do the best I can, but nobody's perfect and there sure are a lot of attractive people out there. I'm 80% sure I can be faithful forever, but anyone who promises you 100% is an unrealistic liar. A 'pretty good' promise is the best anyone can ever hope for, because you can't possibly know who you're going to sleep with next year, or in ten years. Just being honest. You want me to be honest, right?"* – The vow your Reptilian Brain would make at its wedding!

A vow is a plan to remember, but your Reptilian Brain wants you to plan to forget.

Remember, we need to take control and dominate the Reptilian Brain similarly to how we dominate and control our bladders. They are not a part of our human identity.

The benefit of declaring yourself 100% confident and 100% committed when you vow to follow a diet has another very strong benefit which most people don't realize... it allows us to 100% separate the Reptilian Brain's impulses from our own. See, if you're willing to draw a crystal-clear line in the sand about a particular food trigger and/or food behavior, then any thought, feeling, or impulse which suggests you might ever cross it again can be immediately dismissed as nothing more than your Pig Squealing for its junk. A 100% clear and confident commitment is a thinking tool which makes it possible to hear the Pig Squeal *(that seductive inner dialogue which suggests you're going to break your plan)* ...so you can pause and choose wisely!

Finally, as outlined in my original bestselling book "Never Binge Again", we use the word "never" in a kind of funky way, the same way we might tell a 2 year old they can NEVER cross the street without holding our hands, even though we know in five or six years we'll teach them to look both ways and cross on their own. Two year olds are too immature to even consider the possibility of crossing the street by themselves – we don't want that image in their brain lest they dart out when we're not looking. Similarly, our Reptilian Brains act like 2 year olds with food, so we have to tell them our rules are "set in stone forever" and we will "never break or change them", even though we know we very well may change them as a result of experimentation and/or new knowledge obtained at any time. *(I recommend you never change your rules without at least 24 hours delay – this way you won't do it on impulse to feed your Reptilian Brain in the moment.)*

You CAN commit 100%. You CAN say "never" and/or "always" about your food rules and diet. In fact, in my experience it's the only mindset that works!

INSTRUCTIONS: a) Place a checkmark next to the Common Squeal Title above if it was already included in your list of "Out of the Gate Squeals" in Exercise 3A above, then write this *Common Squeal Number* next to the line representing the Squeal in Exercise 3A.(b) If this Squeal bothers you, please underline and circle the reasoning within the detailed explanation above that exposes the half-truth and/or logical distortion your Pig relies on above. Why is this Squeal a lie? Take notes in the margins if need be; (c) If you find a Common Squeal which DOES seem alluring to you but was NOT in your list of "out of the gate" Squeals, add it to Exercise 3A and follow the same instructions above.

COMMON SQUEAL #11 – "YOU CAN'T POSSIBLY GET THROUGH THE HOLIDAYS, DINNER WITH FAMILY, UNEXPECTED RESTAURANT TRIPS, TRAVEL, AND OTHER 'EXCEPTIONS' WITHOUT BREAKING YOUR DIET!"

Most people at some point have been derailed from their diet by an unexpected party, restaurant trip, travel, and other 'exceptions' to their daily routine. However, most of my clients can and do successfully overcome these obstacles by using what I call the "2nd Rung of the Archery Target." See, in many (if not most) cases all that's necessary is advanced planning to carefully define a different set of conditional boundaries for "the exceptions."

For example, maybe you don't eat bread on your diet at all during your everyday routine. This is your "bulls eye" on your personal dietary archery target. Well, most archery targets have more than one rung. Perhaps "I never eat bread" is the daily target for which you aim, but you expand it to say "except when I'm at a family dinner and/or in a restaurant, when I may have up to two pieces, but no more than twice per calendar week." This becomes your well defined '2nd rung.' *(You can even define a third rung which says "or up to four pieces on Thanksgiving, Christmas, and New Year's).*

This works because you've made a clear decision beforehand, and the broader rungs, like the bullseye, have very clearly defined boundaries. It's not "unlimited bread" when you "make a mistake" at a restaurant dinner with Mom, but "two pieces, no more than twice per week."

Remember, decisions wear down your willpower, so you can surmount most difficult situations by researching and deciding beforehand.

When you'll be traveling, it's helpful to research food options online before you go, write down hypothetical plan of exactly what you're going to eat the next day each night before bed, and consider carrying extra, healthy calories with you. *(Keeping almonds or dried chickpeas in your purse, for example, which you can throw on your salad at a restaurant so you won't be tempted to order less healthy options).*

> INSTRUCTIONS: a) Place a checkmark next to the Common Squeal Title above if it was already included in your list of "Out of the Gate Squeals" in Exercise 3A above, then write this *Common Squeal Number* next to the line representing the Squeal in Exercise 3A.(b) If this Squeal bothers you, please underline and circle the reasoning within the detailed explanation above that exposes the half-truth and/or logical distortion your Pig relies on above. Why is this Squeal a lie? Take notes in the

margins if need be; (c) If you find a Common Squeal which DOES seem alluring to you but was NOT in your list of "out of the gate" Squeals, add it to Exercise 3A and follow the same instructions above.

COMMON SQUEAL #12 – "I DON'T HAVE ENOUGH TIME TO EAT HEALTHY AND/OR STAY ON MY DIET!"

Alternate forms of this irrational, confidence destroying belief are that travel, work, children, and/or other commitments create too hectic a schedule to permit healthy eating. None of these hold water when you examine them more carefully under the light of day, however, because it takes MORE time and energy to recover from eating badly than it does to source healthy food when you're traveling and plan out how and when you're going to get and eat it. Plus, eating badly steals your ability to concentrate, your productivity, and your self-confidence.

In other words, you'll be MORE productive and have MORE time in your day if you eat healthy than if you break your diet because it takes a lot out of you to process sugar, flour, salt, excitotoxins, and all the other "food like substances" you'll find in those bags, boxes, and containers.

It's easier to stay on your diet than to break it, even if your Reptilian Brain desperately wants you to believe otherwise! That's why planning healthy eating should always be among your absolute first priorities. If you have time to check Facebook, email, etc., then you certainly have time to stay on your diet.

INSTRUCTIONS: a) Place a checkmark next to the Common Squeal Title above if it was already included in your list of "Out of the Gate Squeals" in Exercise 3A above, then write this *Common Squeal Number* next to the line representing the Squeal in Exercise 3A. (b) If this Squeal bothers you, please underline and circle the reasoning within the detailed explanation above that exposes the half-truth and/or logical distortion your Pig relies on above. Why is this Squeal a lie? Take notes in the margins if need be; (c) If you find a Common Squeal which DOES seem alluring to you but was NOT in your list of "out of the gate" Squeals, add it to Exercise 3A and follow the same instructions above.

COMMON SQUEAL #13 – "DIETING IS JUST TOO HARD!"

Alternate forms of this lie are "I'll starve", "There's nothing else to eat", "Can't possibly get enough calories, nutrition, etc.", "It's just too difficult."

The first thing to do when you hear this Reptilian thought in your head is examine whether there's ANY truth to it. Is your diet too restrictive? Are your authentic nutritional and caloric needs being met? Check with a nutritionist, dietitian, doctor, or one of the online nutritional calculators by inputting a few days' worth of what you actually ate. *(Cronometer.com and My-FitnessPal.com are pretty good.)* If you are indeed not getting enough calories and nutrition to sustain yourself without losing more than a pound or two per week then you'll need to make some adjustments. See Squeal #8 for more on why it's necessary to lose weight *slowly* in most cases.

You should NOT be starving. There should be NO realistic chance we are going to find your bones by the refrigerator tomorrow morning. You may FEEL like you're starving, but you need to evaluate and set your dietary rules such that you know intellectually this is only a feeling, and feelings aren't facts! You need to really believe that your diet won't let you starve to death if you miss one meal.

Then, when your Reptilian Brain says it's too hard to stick to your diet, tell it that it's actually MUCH harder to be overweight, frustrated, discouraged and disgusted with oneself. You get to choose which "hard" you want to face... the "hard" of dieting is actually much easier to deal with when you really think about it.

Finally, ask yourself what you can take with you, have in the car, eat beforehand, stop at a grocery store, etc. when you're out of the house, because that's when most people think it's too hard. *(That and in the evening – which is the subject of an entirely separate book "The End of Nighttime Overeating" available at www.NeverBingeAgainBooks.com)*

COMMON SQUEAL #14 – "ALONE TIME IS NOT COMPLETE WITHOUT AN OVEREATING BINGE!"

When nobody else is around it's very likely your Reptilian Brain will say "Thank God! We are finally alone. Now we can binge and nobody will know. Yippee!!!"

But this is not true because, at minimum, YOU will know! Plus, being alone is a great opportunity to do many things besides overeating: Read a book, take a nap, organize the house, start a new project, call a friend, meditate, do some yoga, research a healthy new dish to cook, see a movie, do a puzzle, take a walk, enjoy nature, look at pictures, sing out loud, do some art, play an instrument, etc.

Alone time is precious, but your Reptilian Brain would like you to squander it solely on its junk!

```
INSTRUCTIONS: a) Place a checkmark next to the Common
Squeal Title above if it was already included in your
list of "Out of the Gate Squeals" in Exercise 3A above,
then write this Common Squeal Number next to the line
representing the Squeal in Exercise 3A.(b) If this Squeal
bothers you, please underline and circle the reasoning
within the detailed explanation above that exposes the
half-truth and/or logical distortion your Pig relies
on above. Why is this Squeal a lie? Take notes in the
margins if need be; (c) If you find a Common Squeal which
DOES seem alluring to you but was NOT in your list of
"out of the gate" Squeals, add it to Exercise 3A and
follow the same instructions above.
```

COMMON SQUEAL #15 – IT DOESN'T MATTER WHAT RULES I MAKE TO CUT ADDICTIVE THINGS OUT OF MY DIET BECAUSE MY REPTILIAN BRAIN WILL ALWAYS FIND SOMETHING ELSE TO OVEREAT! THERE'S SIMPLY NO END TO THINGS I COULD BINGE ON!!

In theory, this lie seems to hold at least some water. After all, there are an almost infinite number of different delectable foods available to us in our modern civilization. It seems one of the things we are best at today is creating delicious foods that destroy us! So, at first glance it SEEMS like there will always be something else to overeat...

But in practice I find that if people are simply persistent in updating their dietary rules as they discover the things their particular Reptilian Brain loves, most run out of binge foods within a few rounds. In other words, your Reptilian Brain may find "something else" to over-eat the first, second, or even third time you tighten up your rules, but shortly thereafter it will be OUT of ammunition!

```
INSTRUCTIONS: a) Place a checkmark next to the Common
Squeal Title above if it was already included in your
list of "Out of the Gate Squeals" in Exercise 3A above,
then write this Common Squeal Number next to the line
representing the Squeal in Exercise 3A.(b) If this Squeal
bothers you, please underline and circle the reasoning
within the detailed explanation above that exposes the
```

half-truth and/or logical distortion your Pig relies on above. Why is this Squeal a lie? Take notes in the margins if need be; (c) If you find a Common Squeal which DOES seem alluring to you but was NOT in your list of "out of the gate" Squeals, add it to Exercise 3A and follow the same instructions above.

COMMON SQUEAL #16 - YOU WON'T BE ABLE TO DISTINGUISH THE REPTILIAN BRAIN'S THOUGHTS AND IMPULSES FROM YOUR OWN HUMAN DESIRES.

The fear of being unable able to effectively discern the Reptilian Brain's desires from your own constructive aims is very common. However, it can be entirely eliminated by ensuring your dietary rules are 100% unambiguous and clear. See, if we artificially define any thought, feeling, impulse, or desire which suggests we will ever break our dietary rules in even the smallest of ways, and if the rules themselves are crystal clear, it becomes EASY to discern these destructive thoughts from our more human, constructive aims.

For example, if I make a dietary rule which says "I will only ever eat chocolate on the last three days of the calendar month" then what could my Reptilian Brain possibly say to get me to do otherwise that I wouldn't immediately recognize as a destructive thought emanating from it? There's nothing!

On the other hand, if I have a vague rule like "I avoid chocolate 90% of the time and indulge the other 10%" then when I hear "how about a little piece of chocolate NOW?" I have no way of knowing if that's ME or my Reptilian Brain... because it's unclear when the 90% applies and when the 10% applies.

If you're having trouble discerning between your Reptilian Brain's thoughts and your own, it's virtually certain there is some ambiguity in your dietary rules. Go back and clean that up by adding more specificity and you will NOT be confused any longer!

For more details on how to do this please read a FREE copy of bestselling book "Never Binge Again" or "101 Best Food Rules" *(which is a paid book.)*

INSTRUCTIONS: a) Place a checkmark next to the Common Squeal Title above if it was already included in your list of "Out of the Gate Squeals" in Exercise 3A above, then write this *Common Squeal Number* next to the line representing the Squeal in Exercise 3A.(b) If this Squeal bothers you, please underline and circle the reasoning within the detailed explanation above that exposes the half-truth and/or logical distortion your Pig relies on above. Why is this Squeal a lie? Take notes in the margins if need be; (c) If you find a Common Squeal which DOES seem alluring to you but was NOT in your list of "out of the gate" Squeals, add it to Exercise 3A and follow the same instructions above.

COMMON SQUEAL #17 – NOBODY WILL WANT TO EAT WITH YOU IF YOU DON'T EAT _____. YOU WILL BECOME A SOCIAL OUTCAST!

ALTERNATE FORMS: You'll be a weirdo. You'll be socially isolated. You'll have to awkwardly explain yourself all the time. You won't have any friends or family to be with comfortably anymore.

Social forces surrounding food are powerful in our society. There must've been a time during our evolution when it was dangerous to refuse to eat what everyone else was, probably because food was often scarce and the labor of every member of the tribe was necessary for its survival. Moreover, taking care of sick and/or weak people in the tribe consumed valuable resources. And warring tribes often "broke bread" to signal the end of their wars and reassure each other they were together as allies, not visiting to rape and pillage.

Accordingly, in the "old days" people didn't really have the luxury of eating individualistically. It wasn't just a matter of "you're a weirdo but do what you want"... it was more a matter of "eat what we're eating or we'll kill you!" Or else, perhaps you'd be left behind to fend for yourself without the protection of the tribe. Either way, if you didn't eat what everyone else ate, you were kinda-sorta screwed in a big way!

Today these pressures don't exist in reality, but I believe they are hard wired into our neurology. We just "feel wrong" when we're with a group and not partaking in the things THEY are all eating.

The lie in the idea that nobody will want to eat with you if you don't eat what they do, however, isn't so much in the fact that they WANT you to eat what they're eating (they do!)...

It's that you really don't HAVE to. Feelings aren't facts. There are several ways you can assuage the psychological needs of your compadres at a meal. None of them involve debating about whether a food is healthy for them or explaining why you don't eat it. All of them involve sidestepping the issue and addressing their social needs instead. Those needs are (1) to be loved and to extend love to you as a member of their tribe; (2) to feel comfortable with what THEY are eating without being made to feel guilty. As discussed previously, you can accomplish both of these things by simply asking for something you CAN eat or drink. "My stomach is still a little too full of lunch. Do you have any mint tea by any chance?" or "I'm cold, do you happen to have a sweater?" Give them something they CAN give you.

Another perspective to consider is that if you love these people, you're worried about getting together with, or even *like* them a little bit... don't you want them to live a long, healthy life? If nobody goes first, and everyone just does what the "average" person is doing with food, then all your friends and family are likely to continue getting "average" health results... and average health results are AWFUL!

According to the World Health Organization 67.9% of adults are overweight in the United States alone. _That's two out of three people!_ And, at the time of publishing this book:

→ **Worldwide obesity since 1975 has TRIPLED!** More than 1.9 Billion adults are overweight and 650 million obese!

→ **Diabetes has increased by 80.8%!** Diabetic adults live with double the risk of heart attack and stroke—*AND*—a seriously increased risk of blindness and kidney failure. *Yet "simple lifestyle measures have shown to be effective in preventing or delaying the onset of type 2 diabetes" – most notably to "achieve and maintain a healthy body weight," "eat a healthy diet," and "be physically active."*

→ **Cardiovascular disease is responsible for 31% of global deaths!** But "most cardiovascular disease can be prevented by addressing behavioral risk factors—*primarily "unhealthy diet, obesity, and lack of exercise!"*

→ **30% to 50% of cancers can be prevented, and dietary modification is an important approach to cancer control.** *"There is a link between overweight and obesity to many types of cancer such as esophagus, colorectum, breast, endometrium and kidney [...] Regular physical activity and the maintenance of a healthy body weight, along with a healthy diet, considerably reduce cancer risk"*

To be average and go along with the crowd is to strive for illness and infirmity, so perhaps you might think about "fitting in" as something undesirable. You can choose to be a healthy leader for your friends, family, and colleagues instead. If you care about these people, someone has to go first. Someone has to become a shining example that it's possible to opt out of the madness. And your healthy results will do more to convince them than anything you could ever point out to them scientifically. So stop worrying about "fitting in" with your friends and family and be a role model for them instead! If you love them, even a little bit, it's the right thing to do!

INSTRUCTIONS: a) Place a checkmark next to the Common Squeal Title above if it was already included in your list of "Out of the Gate Squeals" in Exercise 3A above, then write this *Common Squeal Number* next to the line representing the Squeal in Exercise 3A.(b) If this Squeal bothers you, please underline and circle the reasoning within the detailed explanation above that exposes the half-truth and/or logical distortion your Pig relies on above. Why is this Squeal a lie? Take notes in the margins if need be; (c) If you find a Common Squeal which DOES seem alluring to you but was NOT in your list of "out of the gate" Squeals, add it to Exercise 3A and follow the same instructions above.

COMMON SQUEAL #18 - YOU CAN'T LET FOOD GO TO WASTE – YOU MUST EAT IT RATHER THAN THROWING IT OUT!

ALTERNATE FORMS: "It was on sale." "Available at a friend's house for free." "Was going to be thrown out." "Going bad, etc."

This one is easy - you are not a human garbage can, your body is a sacred vessel. If you've defined a rule for yourself to distinguish healthy vs. junk food (or healthy vs. unhealthy food behaviors) then anything on the wrong side of the line is poisonous to you, and you wouldn't eat a little left over arsenic to avoid throwing it out, would you!?

INSTRUCTIONS: a) Place a checkmark next to the Common Squeal Title above if it was already included in your list of "Out of the Gate Squeals" in Exercise 3A above, then write this *Common Squeal Number* next to the line representing the Squeal in Exercise 3A.(b) If this Squeal bothers you, please underline and circle the reasoning within the detailed explanation above that exposes the half-truth and/or logical distortion your Pig relies on above. Why is this Squeal a lie? Take notes in the margins if need be; (c) If you find a Common Squeal which DOES seem alluring to you but was NOT in your list of "out of the gate" Squeals, add it to Exercise 3A and follow the same instructions above.

COMMON SQUEAL #19 – WE CAN'T MAKE AND FOLLOW ANY DIETARY RULES. DIETARY RULES ARE A FORM RESTRICTION, AND ANY RESTRICTION, EVEN MENTAL RESTRICTION, CAUSES A BINGE. WE HAVE TO EAT INTUITIVELY AND MINDFULLY WITH NO REGARDS FOR ANYTHING ELSE.

ALTERNATE FORMS: It's very bad to label ANY food as healthy vs. unhealthy. Deprivation leads to binging. We have to "allow" every type of food.

Some people are able to find peace with food through strictly intuitive eating. Eat when you're hungry, stop when you're full, stay present and mindful during the whole experience. It's great advice in theory, and if it works for you, more power to you! But I find it does not work for the vast majority of my clients.

See, trusting our bodies natural instincts may have worked exceptionally well when we evolved in the tropics, but today we face extraordinary economic forces designed to hijack our natural instincts.

We're living in unprecedented times...

Big Food spends billions to engineer *food-like substances* which press our pleasure buttons in ways evolution did NOT prepare us to handle...

Then they package these artificial concentrations of starch, sugar, fat, salt, and excitotoxins to make them APPEAR healthy...

And spend even more on advertising to make us THINK we need them!

Did you know there are over 5,000 food messages per year coming at us through the air-waves and the internet...almost none of which are about whole fruits and vegetables?

Most people think advertising doesn't affect them, but this belief actually lowers sales resis-tance—*so the industry has us EXACTLY where they want us!* Dancing bears, bells, and whistles compel us to "look for love" at the bottom of a bag, box, or container... but trust me, it's NOT there, I've checked!!

There's actually flavored cardboard legally in our food system. Flavored cardboard! Doesn't someone have to stand up and say it's WRONG to eat that? A LOT of what we are being offered as "food" is really NOT. It's an addictive "food-like-substance", which is designed to FOOL our intuition. So what FEELS like the right thing to eat is often really NOT. We have to accept that our hungry and full meters have likely been broken by industry, so it's necessary to make more intellectual decisions about food, at least until you've got most of the junk out of your system.

For a detailed discussion on the different between Never Binge Again's rules-based approach vs. the Intuitive Eating approach please listen to this podcast interview at your convenience (FREE):

https://www.neverbingeagain.com/TheBlog/psychology-of-eating/intuitive-eating-vs-never-binge-again/

> INSTRUCTIONS: a) Place a checkmark next to the Common Squeal Title above if it was already included in your list of "Out of the Gate Squeals" in Exercise 3A above, then write this *Common Squeal Number* next to the line representing the Squeal in Exercise 3A.(b) If this Squeal bothers you, please underline and circle the reasoning within the detailed explanation above that exposes the half-truth and/or logical distortion your Pig relies on above. Why is this Squeal a lie? Take notes in the margins if need be; (c) If you find a Common Squeal which DOES seem alluring to you but was NOT in your list of "out of the gate" Squeals, add it to Exercise 3A and follow the same instructions above.

COMMON SQUEAL #20 – XYZ FOOD "CALLS TO" ME TOO STRONGLY!

ALTERNATE FORMS: Can't resist – the bagel/chocolate bar/pizza, etc. is speaking to me.

That's your Reptilian Brain speaking, NOT the food. Can food really talk? When was the last time you had an actual conversation with a bagel, chocolate bar, or piece of pizza?

The idea that food can speak to you is always coming from your destructive self. Recognize and ignore this please!

> INSTRUCTIONS: a) Place a checkmark next to the Common Squeal Title above if it was already included in your list of "Out of the Gate Squeals" in Exercise 3A above, then write this *Common Squeal Number* next to the line representing the Squeal in Exercise 3A.(b) If this Squeal bothers you, please underline and circle the reasoning within the detailed explanation above that exposes the half-truth and/or logical distortion your Pig relies on above. Why is this Squeal a lie? Take notes in the

```
margins if need be; (c) If you find a Common Squeal which
DOES seem alluring to you but was NOT in your list of
"out of the gate" Squeals, add it to Exercise 3A and
follow the same instructions above.
```

COMMON SQUEAL #21 – PICKING AND NOSHING

"You won't be able to help but pick and nosh a little taste here and there while you're baking, preparing food, etc." Alternate Forms: Eating standing up. Eating while baking and/or cooking. Taking little bites from other people's plates. Grazing problems.

Your Reptilian Brain has strong memories of constant picking, noshing, and grazing while you're preparing food and/or just in the kitchen. But there are several things you can do to help eliminate this behavior entirely:

➜ Repeat the following mantra "Food is not my food until it's on my plate"...

➜ Put your fork down between every bite

➜ Don't accept the need to taste test while cooking and baking. Instead, have someone else taste it for you, or make the adjustments the next time you prepare and/or bake the same thing!

➜ Consider three meals and one snack per day, with clear definitions for what constitutes a meal and a snack, as well as how much time needs to pass between them.

➜ Finally, make damn sure you forgive yourself with dignity if you mindlessly nosh on something in the beginning. Because this is an impulsive behavior, it may take you a bit of time to become fully aware and implement your no-noshing rule. Mistakes are common. On the other hand, don't forgive yourself too easily. Teach yourself to become *more* aware in situations where you tend to nosh and remind yourself not to *before* you enter those situations in the future.

➜ And whatever you do... don't let a little bite activate the 'screw it, I blew it' squeal. If anything, each time you become aware of one of those little bite episodes you are actually getting *closer* to being able to avoid them.

```
INSTRUCTIONS: a) Place a checkmark next to the Common
Squeal Title above if it was already included in your
list of "Out of the Gate Squeals" in Exercise 3A above,
then write this Common Squeal Number next to the line
representing the Squeal in Exercise 3A. (b) If this Squeal
```

bothers you, please underline and circle the reasoning within the detailed explanation above that exposes the half-truth and/or logical distortion your Pig relies on above. Why is this Squeal a lie? Take notes in the margins if need be; (c) If you find a Common Squeal which DOES seem alluring to you but was NOT in your list of "out of the gate" Squeals, add it to Exercise 3A and follow the same instructions above.

COMMON SQUEAL #22 - OTHER PEOPLE ARE IMPOSSIBLE AND YOU SIMPLY MUST BINGE TO PLEASE THEM

Many people fear they'll be unable to stick to a diet because of the "food pushers" around them. "It's too important to my mother, sister, aunt, father, brother, etc. for me to eat their food" they say...

But NOBODY can make you overeat without your permission! Nobody can instantaneously change your definition of healthy vs. unhealthy food. Nobody can alter the dietary rules you write down in black and white.

It's exceptionally rare for people to be kidnapped, tied down, and force-fed food off their diet. You have autonomy in what you choose to put in your mouth in 99.9% of the world, and nobody can control your hands, arms, legs, mouth and tongue.

If you analyze the situation where it seems you were unable to resist a "food pusher", you'll find the other person was looking for acceptance, love, and permission to eat what they wanted to, and you simply need to find a way to make them feel loved WITHOUT putting garbage in your mouth. Don't argue with them, love them instead.

INSTRUCTIONS: a) Place a checkmark next to the Common Squeal Title above if it was already included in your list of "Out of the Gate Squeals" in Exercise 3A above, then write this *Common Squeal Number* next to the line representing the Squeal in Exercise 3A. (b) If this Squeal bothers you, please underline and circle the reasoning within the detailed explanation above that exposes the half-truth and/or logical distortion your Pig relies on above. Why is this Squeal a lie? Take notes in the margins if need be; (c) If you find a Common Squeal which DOES seem alluring to you but was NOT in your list of

```
"out of the gate" Squeals, add it to Exercise 3A and
follow the same instructions above.
```

COMMON SQUEAL #23 – BEING TOO FULL IS TOO MUCH OF A TRIGGER AND YOU CAN'T AVOID IT

It seems counterintuitive, but some people are prone to overeat a LOT more when they find they've gotten too full. This is probably an evolutionary mechanism: If we lived in an environment where food was scarce for long periods of time, then being full would be a sign it was suddenly available. "The harvest is finally here, let's hoard the food while we can!"

But both the idea that you must inevitably get too full AND the idea you must overeat more when you do are illogical. It's entirely possible to eat normal amounts and avoid getting too full. It's also entirely possible to recognize when this urge has been triggered and decline to engage. One simply must be aware of the problem.

```
INSTRUCTIONS: a) Place a checkmark next to the Common
Squeal Title above if it was already included in your
list of "Out of the Gate Squeals" in Exercise 3A above,
then write this Common Squeal Number next to the line
representing the Squeal in Exercise 3A.(b) If this Squeal
bothers you, please underline and circle the reasoning
within the detailed explanation above that exposes the
half-truth and/or logical distortion your Pig relies
on above. Why is this Squeal a lie? Take notes in the
margins if need be; (c) If you find a Common Squeal which
DOES seem alluring to you but was NOT in your list of
"out of the gate" Squeals, add it to Exercise 3A and
follow the same instructions above.
```

COMMON SQUEAL #24 – YOU WILL EVENTUALLY GET A COLD OR A FLU AND WON'T BE ABLE TO KEEP TO YOUR DIET

This one is kind of simple – one needs to eat HEALTHIER when they're ill, not worse. Following your dietary rules should make you feel better, not worse. If you're too sick to cook you can order in something healthy or call a friend/family member to help. There's NO logic to eating poorly when you're ill.

If you're actively dieting *(i.e. losing weight through a caloric deficit)*, it might be a good idea to slightly increase your caloric intake to maintenance level when you're sick. But, despite what

The Never Binge Again *Workbook*

your Pig may say, being sick doesn't require you to eat 5,000 calories instead of 2,000. On top of this, if you eat too much your body will be tasked with digesting all that food, and this can take energy away from the healing process. In fact, animals often stop eating when they become sick to preserve their energy so they can heal quickly. But with our broken 'hunger' meters we've learned to associate any discomfort with hunger. So when that flu comes on, instead of gorging, you might consider eating *healthier* and drinking a lot of fluids. Plus, think about it, is it worth undoing months of weight loss because of a flu? The Pig would love you to think so, but when the fever clears, will you agree with it?

> INSTRUCTIONS: a) Place a checkmark next to the Common Squeal Title above if it was already included in your list of "Out of the Gate Squeals" in Exercise 3A above, then write this *Common Squeal Number* next to the line representing the Squeal in Exercise 3A. (b) If this Squeal bothers you, please underline and circle the reasoning within the detailed explanation above that exposes the half-truth and/or logical distortion your Pig relies on above. Why is this Squeal a lie? Take notes in the margins if need be; (c) If you find a Common Squeal which DOES seem alluring to you but was NOT in your list of "out of the gate" Squeals, add it to Exercise 3A and follow the same instructions above.

COMMON SQUEAL #25 – "C'MON, YOU CAN GET AWAY WITH IT!"

ALTERNATE FORMS: We're thin enough, we exercised enough, we've been good for enough days, we're close enough to goal weight, we just got those nice compliments about our looks lately, etc.

Jack Trimpey is the author of Rational Recovery. I once heard his wife say in an interview that addiction will always expand to the tolerance which surrounds it. Translation: Your Reptilian Brain will endeavor to get away with whatever you LET it get away with, and not one smidgeon less.

On the other hand, the Reptilian Brain is inferior to your human decisions, and if you choose to exercise your authority it has no choice but to behave like a submissive animal and bend to YOUR wishes. Therefore, if you set an enforceable boundary and steady your commitment to stick with it no matter what, what the Reptilian Brain can get away with is preciously small!

83

Another strategy to help you with this is to gradually keep raising the bar. Set better, healthier goals as you progress—taking care not to become too thin or weak of course. That way you train your Reptilian Brain to get away with progressively less, tamping down its tendency to try for more.

There are three other perspective which may help you: First, you will lose the experience of long-term compliance if you break your diet, even if you could get away with it in the short run. You'll never know what it feels like to confidently know you kept to it for six months, a year, etc. Second, compliments are meant to help you enjoy your experience, not to facilitate self-destruction. Finally, you don't have to live you00r life based entirely on the pleasure principle which says you must maximize your short-term pleasure. Instead, you can choose to forgo certain short-term pleasures in order that you might experience others in the long-run, and accomplish more longer-term, bigger goals. *(Like permanent weight loss, for example.)*

```
INSTRUCTIONS: a) Place a checkmark next to the Common
Squeal Title above if it was already included in your
list of "Out of the Gate Squeals" in Exercise 3A above,
then write this Common Squeal Number next to the line
representing the Squeal in Exercise 3A.(b) If this Squeal
bothers you, please underline and circle the reasoning
within the detailed explanation above that exposes the
half-truth and/or logical distortion your Pig relies
on above. Why is this Squeal a lie? Take notes in the
margins if need be; (c) If you find a Common Squeal which
DOES seem alluring to you but was NOT in your list of
"out of the gate" Squeals, add it to Exercise 3A and
follow the same instructions above.
```

COMMON SQUEAL #26 – "THAT MEAL SUCKED EGGS, WE NEED A BETTER ONE."

Alternate Forms: Crappy food at the wedding, party, event, etc. "We deserve something richer, starchier, sugary, etc.

It's not uncommon for the Reptilian Brain to make you *feel* you "deserve" another, better tasting, more satiating meal when you've just experienced one you didn't enjoy. But the truth is, if one meal is disappointing there's always another one coming up in a few hours, or the next morning at worst. You can certainly resolve to make an extra effort to ensure the next meal is satisfying but overeating at this one will only lead to more suffering.

Plus, what's more important? The Pig enjoying a great big Binge or you keeping to your diet? You know the answer!

Life isn't a pain-free experience, it's OK to be disappointed sometimes. *(Make sure your Reptilian Brain knows this!)*

> INSTRUCTIONS: a) Place a checkmark next to the Common Squeal Title above if it was already included in your list of "Out of the Gate Squeals" in Exercise 3A above, then write this *Common Squeal Number* next to the line representing the Squeal in Exercise 3A.(b) If this Squeal bothers you, please underline and circle the reasoning within the detailed explanation above that exposes the half-truth and/or logical distortion your Pig relies on above. Why is this Squeal a lie? Take notes in the margins if need be; (c) If you find a Common Squeal which DOES seem alluring to you but was NOT in your list of "out of the gate" Squeals, add it to Exercise 3A and follow the same instructions above.

COMMON SQUEAL #27 – "YOU'LL EVENTUALLY HAVE TO EAT AT A BUFFET WITH NO CLEAR PORTION SIZES (OR INGREDIENT LISTS) AND THEN YOU'LL BLOW YOUR DIET FOR SURE!"

A lot of people feel they can't keep to their diet when faced with dining in a buffet restaurant situation. But there are several very practical ways to control the Reptilian Brain at a buffet. First, you may wish to ensure HALF your plate is comprised of only vegetables, and then resolve to NEVER go back for seconds. You can also resolve to have NO deserts at a buffet, or at the very least limit yourself to ONE helping.

In other words, make special "exception" rules for buffets with very clear boundaries. Then try not to eat at a buffet more than twice a month. These two things combined should prevent the buffet from doing too much damage to your diet.

> INSTRUCTIONS: a) Place a checkmark next to the Common Squeal Title above if it was already included in your list of "Out of the Gate Squeals" in Exercise 3A above, then write this *Common Squeal Number* next to the line representing the Squeal in Exercise 3A.(b) If this Squeal bothers you, please underline and circle the reasoning

within the detailed explanation above that exposes the
half-truth and/or logical distortion your Pig relies
on above. Why is this Squeal a lie? Take notes in the
margins if need be; (c) If you find a Common Squeal which
DOES seem alluring to you but was NOT in your list of
"out of the gate" Squeals, add it to Exercise 3A and
follow the same instructions above.

COMMON SQUEAL #28 - "JUST ONE MORE DAY OF JUNK PLEASE"

This is a variation of the "let's start tomorrow" lie but is listed here because there's a very specific retort which works wonders. When your Reptilian Brain says "just one more day of junk" you can think to yourself "just one more day of healthy eating!"

See, you can always change your dietary rules with due reflection (in writing) and a 24 to 48 hour delay before the changes take effect... so if YOU really want whatever junk the Reptilian Brain is suggesting you have for "just one more day", you can make that day TOMORROW instead of today. 99% of the time you won't still be craving whatever the thing happened to be when you get home and have time to journal about whether or not to change your dietary rules. The moment will pass, the craving will have died down, and you will have pushed the destructive Reptilian thought out of your mind long enough to have eaten healthy for the day.

INSTRUCTIONS: a) Place a checkmark next to the Common
Squeal Title above if it was already included in your
list of "Out of the Gate Squeals" in Exercise 3A above,
then write this *Common Squeal Number* next to the line
representing the Squeal in Exercise 3A. (b) If this Squeal
bothers you, please underline and circle the reasoning
within the detailed explanation above that exposes the
half-truth and/or logical distortion your Pig relies
on above. Why is this Squeal a lie? Take notes in the
margins if need be; (c) If you find a Common Squeal which
DOES seem alluring to you but was NOT in your list of
"out of the gate" Squeals, add it to Exercise 3A and
follow the same instructions above.

COMMON SQUEAL #29 – THIS WILL TAKE TOO MUCH ONGOING WORK

Clients often suggest to me that it will be difficult to lose weight forever because it requires constant vigilance and alertness. "It's too much work" they say, and this saps their confidence and belief in themselves... but it's not at all true, and it's NOT unlike many other things you're already doing in life.

What you do need are simple, clear rules which define healthy vs. unhealthy eating for you personally. If you know where the lines are, it becomes much easier to recognize the thoughts and feelings which attempt to compel you to cross them. If you DO have ultra-clear rules in place, you CAN relax after a few months.

Think of it like this: Suppose I have a rule that says I will only ever eat chocolate again on Saturdays and Sundays. How can I possibly have a "sneaky thought" that compels me to eat a bar on a Wednesday? I can't. Any thought, feeling, or image which suggests I should ever have chocolate on a weekday again will be immediately recognizable as coming from my Reptilian Brain. So, I don't have to be "constantly vigilant" ... I just have to be AWAKE.

A good metaphor might be thinking of yourself as the bouncer at a party. It's easy to recognize a sleazebag trying to get through the door, and no problem at all to keep them from entering because they are SO much weaker than you. *(You are wired to be superior to your Reptilian Brain.)* It's an easy job, but someone always has to do it. If you remove the bouncer from the door then Mr. Sleazebag will be happy to enter. But there's no need to remove the bouncer, however, because it requires VERY little effort once you've crafted your sleazebag recognition skills. You can carry on conversations with others, and just relax and scan for sleazebags in with your peripheral vision.

In psychology there's a metal state called "alert wakefulness." Every mother has seen it in their children. It's where you're just kind of relaxed but awake and looking around to see what's happening, unconsciously processing everything in your environment. For example, I'm awake right now and concentrating 99% of my energy on writing this section, but my patio door looking out on the beach is wide open, and my peripheral vision. Occasionally I glance out to take in what's happening outside. If there were a big storm approaching, I'd know it was time to close the patio door. I'd have plenty of notice. I don't have to consciously stress about whether rain, wind, and debris are going to come flooding into my apartment. In fact, I hardly spend ANY mental energy at all on this task. I trust myself to see the signs of the storm. I'd "sense" people fleeing the beach in large numbers, the sky getting darker, and perhaps the wind shifting. This doesn't cause me any stress. I feel perfectly relaxed and able to enjoy my writing (and my life!)

You do the same thing when you're driving. You know the rules of the road. You *(hopefully)* know where you're going. You can talk to people on the phone, listen to music, or write an opera in your head while you drift along the road, just gently aware of what's happening. You occasionally scan the mirrors. Look down at the speedometer. Adjust the pressure on the pedals. You have to do all those things if you're going to drive a car, but you don't need to stress about it. You just accept it as part of your responsibility as a driver.

It's the same with changing the way you eat. At first it requires a significant mental effort as you learn the new rules of the road and build a new scanning routine into your everyday mental activity. But rest assured it gets MUCH easier the more you "drive." Yes, you'll always have to be awake and sitting in the driver's seat if you want to get anywhere, but this become effortless with time.

Finally, compare the effort it takes to remain heavier than you'd like to be. It's harder to get off the couch, play with your kids, walk outside, buy clothing that fits, get dressed in the morning, get to the gym or out in nature for some exercise, etc. No, being thinner is actually a lot EASIER than being overweight. What's HARD is being fat.

End of rant.

> INSTRUCTIONS: a) Place a checkmark next to the Common Squeal Title above if it was already included in your list of "Out of the Gate Squeals" in Exercise 3A above, then write this *Common Squeal Number* next to the line representing the Squeal in Exercise 3A. (b) If this Squeal bothers you, please underline and circle the reasoning within the detailed explanation above that exposes the half-truth and/or logical distortion your Pig relies on above. Why is this Squeal a lie? Take notes in the margins if need be; (c) If you find a Common Squeal which DOES seem alluring to you but was NOT in your list of "out of the gate" Squeals, add it to Exercise 3A and follow the same instructions above.

COMMON SQUEAL #30 – TREATING THE REPTILIAN BRAIN AS A SEPARATE ENTITY IS SILLY. "I DON'T REALLY EXIST SEPARATE AND APART FROM YOU" IT SAYS.

You may have noticed that throughout this chapter I've relied upon separating your thoughts into two distinct types: Yours vs. Your Reptilian Brain's. The reason for this is because it's the primary technique I used to recover from compulsive overeating myself, as well as that which has helped hundreds of clients, and tens of thousands of readers around the world. It's more elaborate than this, but the separation underlies the whole thing.

In my own recovery I called my reptilian brain my "Inner Pig", anything outside of my dietary rules "Pig Slop", and anything the Pig said to try and get me to eat off my plan "Pig Squeal." I was never going to publish this "technique" … it was just a weird way I discovered to wake ME up at the moment of temptation. It gave me the extra microseconds I needed to think about what I was doing and consider making the right decision. Slowly but surely it worked miracles for me.

I published the book in 2015 on the request of a business partner, and also because it looked like I might be getting divorced and I didn't want to keep building the businesses I was going to have to tear down if indeed the divorce went through (it did). I had NO idea it was going to take off. I WISH I used another metaphor because a lot of people object to thinking of a "Pig" inside them. It works just as well to think of it as your Reptilian Brain…

But the thing is, the concept of separating your thoughts very clearly in two and treating the lower brain like a fictitious enemy works wonders. I was originally introduced to the idea in a brilliant book on alcoholism called "Rational Recovery" by Jack Trimpey.

Anyway, the key is to understand that binge eating—all addiction really—is a corruption of your survival drive. A kind of hijacking of it by industry. And having a very easy, primitive method to recognize and ignore the erroneous thoughts associated with the unhealthy object of desire is perhaps the ONLY method I've ever found that interrupts what otherwise feels like an oncoming locomotive!

But your Reptilian Brain (or "Inner Pig" if you prefer) doesn't want to be redirected towards health. It knows how effective this technique is. Therefore, it will try every trick in the book, even including the idea that it doesn't exist in the first place, to get you to avoid clearly recognizing and ignoring diet-destroying thoughts. Here's an excerpt from my first book which explains how to cope with this tricky strategy:

```
"You know there's not really a Pig inside you. Therefore,
   none of this 'Dominate the Pig' stuff makes ANY sense
   at all. So why don't you just let me out and Binge
   already!!!?" - Your Pig
```

As discussed previously, the Pig is a language gimmick. There's no real Pig inside you. It's only a concept, even though the dynamic between you and the Pig can be characterized as that which exists between more recently evolved neocortical functions and the mid-brain, where survival impulses originate.

But the Pig is not "just" a language gimmick, it's an incredibly effective language gimmick! In fact, it may be the ONLY way to thoroughly separate your thin-thinking-self from the fat thoughts and feelings which have sabotaged your efforts until this point in life.

And let's bring back our governmental analogy: The continually refined use of language is what allows humans to coordinate and control their impulses so they can participate in a civil society. Language is what separates us from the apes and allows us to articulate the laws which make it possible to live amongst one another.

Language is how we managed to step out of the jungle and move beyond "might makes right" to form a society.

Language is the very fabric of our civilization.

Never Binge Again is a way of using language which can restore full control over your eating and eradicate the ridiculous notion that free will and responsibility don't exist when it comes to toxic pleasure.

The Pig would love you to declare it non-existent so it could Binge.

Cage the Pig and keep it there!

> INSTRUCTIONS: a) Place a checkmark next to the Common Squeal Title above if it was already included in your list of "Out of the Gate Squeals" in Exercise 3A above, then write this *Common Squeal Number* next to the line representing the Squeal in Exercise 3A. (b) If this Squeal bothers you, please underline and circle the reasoning within the detailed explanation above that exposes the half-truth and/or logical distortion your Pig relies on above. Why is this Squeal a lie? Take notes in the

margins if need be; (c) If you find a Common Squeal which DOES seem alluring to you but was NOT in your list of "out of the gate" Squeals, add it to Exercise 3A and follow the same instructions above.

COMMON SQUEAL #31: YOU SHOULD PURSUE PROGRESS, NOT PERFECTION

This is a tricky one too, because the "progress not perfection" mindset is very helpful AFTER you've made a mistake and are trying to get back on track. The problem with "progress not perfection" as a commitment tool when you are proactively trying to hit a goal—especially one which involves avoiding and/or reducing artificial pleasure—is that all it really means is "I'll try for a little while until I don't feel like it anymore, then I'll indulge."

The interesting thing about the "progress not perfection" belief which the Reptilian Brain throws at you is that it will talk out of both sides of its mouth. After a mistake it won't say "Oh well, progress not perfection, just get back up and try again", which is what you're SUPPOSED to do. Instead, it will say "If you're not perfect then you're NOTHING! You made a mistake and are obviously just a pathetic overeater. You might as well just go get us some binge food and we can have us a big old junk food party!"

Am I right or am I right? It only wants to binge and will use ANYTHING against you to persuade you to feed it, but you don't have to fall for this.

The appropriate attitude when you're trying to hit a bullseye on an archery target is to AIM with perfection but forgive yourself with dignity. You want to know exactly where the bulls eye begins and ends. You want to see it with tremendous clarity. Before you let the arrow go, you want to visualize it going into the bullseye as a foregone conclusion. You want to "be" the bullseye – commit with every ounce of your being so that you can purge your mind of doubt and distraction, and direct ALL your mental energy towards hitting your goal...

But if you miss, you're not supposed to say "I'm pathetic" and shoot the rest of the arrows into the air. You're supposed to analyze what went wrong so you can make adjustments in your aim *next time*. Once you've made those adjustments, you're supposed to forgive yourself so you can free all your energy for the commitment to aim with perfection once again. This is how winners win the game!

Commit with perfection but forgive yourself with dignity.

INSTRUCTIONS: a) Place a checkmark next to the Common Squeal Title above if it was already included in your list of "Out of the Gate Squeals" in Exercise 3A above, then write this *Common Squeal Number* next to the line representing the Squeal in Exercise 3A.(b) If this Squeal bothers you, please underline and circle the reasoning within the detailed explanation above that exposes the half-truth and/or logical distortion your Pig relies on above. Why is this Squeal a lie? Take notes in the margins if need be; (c) If you find a Common Squeal which DOES seem alluring to you but was NOT in your list of "out of the gate" Squeals, add it to Exercise 3A and follow the same instructions above.

COMMON SQUEAL #32 – THERE'S NO NEED TO WRITE DOWN MY DIETARY RULES – I CAN KEEP THEM IN MY HEAD

If this irrational idea is bothering you, do me a favor and go look up the research on how witness testimony can change over time. Memory is unfortunately a somewhat fluid phenomenon. We adjust our memory over time so that it can make more sense to us, and often so that it's more pleasing to us. There's a reason the law is required to be in writing. Things which are written down in black and white are much more permanent and authoritative. Without writing things down you're subjecting yourself to unconsciously adjusting your dietary rules due to emotional whim, etc. Write them down please and your confidence/belief will improve!

INSTRUCTIONS: a) Place a checkmark next to the Common Squeal Title above if it was already included in your list of "Out of the Gate Squeals" in Exercise 3A above, then write this *Common Squeal Number* next to the line representing the Squeal in Exercise 3A.(b) If this Squeal bothers you, please underline and circle the reasoning within the detailed explanation above that exposes the half-truth and/or logical distortion your Pig relies on above. Why is this Squeal a lie? Take notes in the margins if need be; (c) If you find a Common Squeal which DOES seem alluring to you but was NOT in your list of "out of the gate" Squeals, add it to Exercise 3A and follow the same instructions above.

COMMON SQUEAL #33 – I DON'T HAVE ENOUGH MONEY TO EAT HEALTHY. HEALTHY FOOD IS TOO EXPENSIVE. I CAN'T AFFORD IT.

Look, what's too expensive is being sick. It's a pay me now or pay me later kind of game.

Plus, it actually costs more to be heavy because you require more sleep, it's more difficult to do things during the day as you drag around the extra weight so your productivity can suffer, and your risk for diet-reversible disease goes way up.

Last, if you think fruit and vegetables are too expensive, you just haven't learned how to shop for them yet. Rather than buy them at a supermarket, look for specialty produce markets in your area. You can often find them in the suburbs. Then go in, place one or two bulk orders. Once the owners have noticed you, tell them you eat a LOT of fruit and vegetables and were wondering if they could offer you a significant discount if you did most of your shopping with them. I find two out of three owners are more than accommodating, and I can get very good (often organic) produce at approximately half the price I'd pay at the supermarket. Some produce is a lot less expensive than others, especially if you shop in season. Make that produce a staple.

It's not that you can't afford to eat healthy, it's more like you can't afford not to!

```
INSTRUCTIONS: a) Place a checkmark next to the Common
Squeal Title above if it was already included in your
list of "Out of the Gate Squeals" in Exercise 3A above,
then write this Common Squeal Number next to the line
representing the Squeal in Exercise 3A.(b) If this Squeal
bothers you, please underline and circle the reasoning
within the detailed explanation above that exposes the
half-truth and/or logical distortion your Pig relies
on above. Why is this Squeal a lie? Take notes in the
margins if need be; (c) If you find a Common Squeal which
DOES seem alluring to you but was NOT in your list of
"out of the gate" Squeals, add it to Exercise 3A and
follow the same instructions above.
```

COMMON SQUEAL #34 – YOU'LL FEEL TOO GUILTY FOR CONTINUING TO HAVE URGES SO EVENTUALLY YOU'LL GIVE IN!

Although cravings will seriously diminish over time if you eliminate and/or dramatically reduce your trigger foods, they never go away 100%. It's always possible to experience one, because we can't cut out our Reptilian Brains, and the behavioral grooves are too deeply myelinated. In other words, the patterns and memories are deep within our brains waiting to be reactivated...

But you need not fear them. They're just a function of your own body, and you can learn how to channel them to more appropriate foods, just like, as a civilized human being, you've learned to channel the urges created by your bladder into the bathroom instead of the living room. You'd never expect yourself to never have the urge to pee again... so expect yourself not to have other biological urges? The idea is to teach yourself what to DO with them, not to eliminate them entirely.

Don't cultivate fear of your own body, cultivate confidence instead!

> INSTRUCTIONS: a) Place a checkmark next to the Common Squeal Title above if it was already included in your list of "Out of the Gate Squeals" in Exercise 3A above, then write this *Common Squeal Number* next to the line representing the Squeal in Exercise 3A. (b) If this Squeal bothers you, please underline and circle the reasoning within the detailed explanation above that exposes the half-truth and/or logical distortion your Pig relies on above. Why is this Squeal a lie? Take notes in the margins if need be; (c) If you find a Common Squeal which DOES seem alluring to you but was NOT in your list of "out of the gate" Squeals, add it to Exercise 3A and follow the same instructions above.

COMMON SQUEAL #35 – OBESITY RUNS IN MY FAMILY SO I'M DOOMED TO BE FAT!

OK, let's look at the hard part of the truth straight on: Research HAS shown a multitude of genes which may predispose people to gain weight. For example, the fat mass and obesity-associated gene (FTO) can be identified in up to 43% of the population. When calorie rich food is constantly available to such people, it's clear they have more trouble limiting intake. Furthermore, obesity related genes can *increase* your appetite and *reduce* your metabolism. Not fair, I know! But it's not destiny either...

Genetics are a part of the equation, not the whole equation. There are plenty of people with the FTO gene, for example, who do NOT manifest obesity. In fact, a recent article in the Harvard School of Public Health summarizing the research into obesity to date states that we are essentially still in the very early stages of studying genetic influence. More importantly, the author goes on to say "genetic factors identified so far make only a small contribution to obesity risk-and that our genes are not our destiny. Many people who carry these so-called "obesity genes" do not become overweight, and healthy lifestyles can counteract these genetic effects."

Part of the illusion one is "doomed" comes from a misunderstanding of statistical relationships. Let's suppose research found a 60% correlation between mothers and daughters regarding obesity. To get the actually amount of the relationship that explained by this association—in other words, how much better would you be at guessing the daughter's weight if you knew only the mother's weight—you have to SQUARE the correlation. That means only 36% of the variance in obesity is accounted for by the genetic relationship...

If math gives you a headache just try to remember this: The numbers you hear about genetic influence on obesity sound bigger than they really are. As near as my trained scientific researcher's eyes can read it you didn't get five crappy cards dealt to you in the obesity poker game, more like one or two. Is that a handicap as compared to people who got five great cards? Sure. But you've still got a few picture cards, and perhaps even an ace up your sleeve if you'll take the time to look for it.

Hope that makes sense.

```
INSTRUCTIONS: a) Place a checkmark next to the Common
Squeal Title above if it was already included in your
list of "Out of the Gate Squeals" in Exercise 3A above,
then write this Common Squeal Number next to the line
representing the Squeal in Exercise 3A.(b) If this Squeal
bothers you, please underline and circle the reasoning
within the detailed explanation above that exposes the
half-truth and/or logical distortion your Pig relies
on above. Why is this Squeal a lie? Take notes in the
margins if need be; (c) If you find a Common Squeal which
DOES seem alluring to you but was NOT in your list of
"out of the gate" Squeals, add it to Exercise 3A and
follow the same instructions above.
```

→ Obesity and Genetics: Nature and Nurture. (2019). Obesity Medicine Association. [Blog post retrieved from https://obesitymedicine.org/obesity-and-genetics/]

→ Genetics are Not Destiny. Harvard T.H. Chan School of Public Health. [Retrieved from https://www.hsph.harvard.edu/obesity-prevention-source/obesity-causes/genes-and-obesity/]

COMMON SQUEAL #36 "POOR ME" – I'VE WASTED MY WHOLE LIFE OVEREATING AND I'M NOT NEARLY THE PERSON I COULD BE BECAUSE OF IT – SO I MIGHT AS WELL NOT BOTHER TRYING TO MAKE USE OF THE REST OF YOUR IT. AFTER ALL, WHAT'S THE POINT OF A FEW GOOD YEARS ON TOP OF ALL THOSE LOUSY ONES?

Sometimes our Reptilian Brains try to tell us that even if we could lose weight permanently, there'd be no point because our life is already essentially wasted. This ignores the fact older people are MOST able to contribute to the world from a point of wisdom and experience however, as well as the fact that your level of productivity, engagement, ability to love and be present, etc. generally skyrockets once you've stopped overeating. In fact, because most people who've significantly overeaten for a major portion of their lives don't ever want to go back, they tend to land on a MUCH HEALTHIER diet and exercise routine than the average person out there. As a result, they have MORE energy, MORE clarity of mind, and MORE purpose than the average person too.

In other words, you CAN make up for lost time. And even if you couldn't, why not live out the balance of your life feeling lighter, freer, and happier?

```
INSTRUCTIONS: a) Place a checkmark next to the Common
Squeal Title above if it was already included in your
list of "Out of the Gate Squeals" in Exercise 3A above,
then write this Common Squeal Number next to the line
representing the Squeal in Exercise 3A.(b) If this Squeal
bothers you, please underline and circle the reasoning
within the detailed explanation above that exposes the
half-truth and/or logical distortion your Pig relies
on above. Why is this Squeal a lie? Take notes in the
margins if need be; (c) If you find a Common Squeal which
DOES seem alluring to you but was NOT in your list of
"out of the gate" Squeals, add it to Exercise 3A and
follow the same instructions above.
```

Exercise 3E) Dealing with Squeals Not Otherwise Covered: Go through your list of "Out of the Gate Squeals" from Exercise 3A above. Have you found the answer to each and every one of those Squeals? If so, move on to Chapter 4. *Otherwise, list out your Remaining Squeals below. What Squeals could you NOT find an answer for in the Common Squeals section?*

PART ONE: WRITING DOWN THE SQUEALS

(i)

_____

_____

_____

(ii)

_____

_____

_____

(iii)

_____

_____

_____

(iv)

_____

_____

_____

(v)

_____

_____

_____

(vi)

_____

_____

_____

(vii)

_____

_____

_____

(vii)

_____

_____

_____

For each one of the above Squeals, do your best on your own to articulate the lie it contains. Remember, there's always a half truth, but there's always also a lie too. There HAS TO BE because it is never necessary to binge and/or break your One Simple Rule. How is your Pig lying to you above?

If you're still stumped, you can do some Google research. For example, I remember when I had a Food Rule which said "I will never again consume any foods and/or drinks with added sodium" my Pig said "C'mon, you do NOT have high blood pressure and you eat extremely healthy otherwise. Is a little sea salt going to kill you?" But I really wanted to stick with this Food Rule because I knew I just felt "icky" the next morning when I added sea salt to my broccoli, etc. And it seemed very difficult for me to just add "a little" salt... when I used it, I really wanted to pour it on! So, I researched the negative effects of added sodium on people who do NOT have high blood pressure and discovered that it increases the risk of hyperbaric strokes. My family is particularly prone to strokes and other cardiovascular events, so the moment I realized this increased the risk the Squeal no longer appealed to me. Check and mate, Pig!

You can also come onto our free reader's forum and ask your peers for help. www.NeverBingeAgainForum.com

Or you can consider our paid coaching programs at www.NeverBingeAgainCoaching.com

But I've done my absolute best to give you the tools to dispute ALL your Squeals without additional help above!

Try not to leave any Squeals unanswered before moving on from this point. However, if you're absolutely stumped on a few Squeals, it's still OK to keep going for now. Just DO reach out for help above please.

(Next Page Please)

PART TWO: ARTICULATING THE LIE
(FINDING THE FALSE LOGIC)

OK, do your best to articulate the lies in the Squeals you just revealed now please. For your convenience they have been numbered to match the template above:

(i)

_____

_____

_____

(ii)

_____

_____

_____

(iii)

_____

_____

_____

(iv)

_____

_____

_____

(v)

_____

_____

_____

(vi)

_____

_____

_____

(vii)

_____

_____

_____

(vii)

_____

_____

_____

Chapter 4

Disempowering "Surprise" Excuses Lingering Beneath the Surface

What we've done to this point is simple, but remarkable. Most people NEVER stop to focus with 100% clarity on even One Simple Rule to which they've committed 100%. As a result, they can't hear their inner food enemy's voice clearly. For them, the ambiguous line between healthy vs. unhealthy behavior means they don't know if a given thought and/or suggestion in their mind is coming from themselves or the Pig. But the moment you clarify where the line is and commit to it, you CAN hear the Pig because you know Pig Squeal is any thought, feeling, impulse, and/or image in your head which suggests you'll EVER cross the line. Is there something in your head that suggests and/or makes you feel like you should cross the line? That's your Pig. Period, end of story.

If you KNOW something is coming from your Pig AND you know that EVERYTHING the Pig says, does, or feels is, by definition *(see the first three chapters of NeverBingeAgain.com available FREE at the website)* designed to get you to binge, then you can simply ignore it. Or you can rationally dispute it, like we did in the exercise above, to make the Squeals even less alluring.

The result is a LOT more confidence that you can follow your One Simple Rule. And that confidence feels great. If you've done the exercises above, you're probably feeling much better about your rule. A good deal of the anxiety has left you. You more or less feel you CAN do this.

Unfortunately, a "lot" more confidence isn't good enough. Here's why: Suppose you feel 90% confident you're going to follow your rule. What that means to your Pig is 9 times out of 10 it won't be able to get out of its Cage, but on the 10th time it probably will. In Pig logic, this means it just needs to try more frequently. *"Ooooooooh – if I try 100 times then we'll get to binge 10 times, right? Yummmmmmmy!!! Let's get to it!" – Your Pig.*

See what I mean?

We ABSOLUTELY MUST GET TO 100% CONFIDENCE or else all we are doing is encouraging the Pig to try more often. Read that sentence again please because it can make all the difference in your success. Nothing less than 100% confidence will be acceptable. And you can reliably get there with the simple exercises in this section no matter how you're feeling right now. You can, you can, you CAN!

How?

The first step is to 100% commit, body mind and soul, to follow your Food Plan forever.

➔ **Food Rule** = a statement which governs a particular trigger food, food behavior, and/or healthy behavior you want to incorporate in your life.

➔ **Food Plan** = all your Food Rules considered as a set. Even if you have only one Food Rule, you have a Food Plan. You'll add more to it later.

What you're actually committing to do FOREVER is follow your Food Plan. You are NOT committing to never changing the Food Rules within it.

You can change the Food Rules within your Food Plan at any time with appropriate forethought and consideration, and a 24-hour delay between the written change and when it takes effect. See the chapter in Never Binge Again on Changing Your Food Plan for details. In fact, in the case of your One Simple Rule, at first, we are committing to re-evaluating your Food Plan in 10 days. We still write our Food *Rule* as if it were forever so we can present it to our Pig's as if it were set in stone. But the Food Plan is going to be re-evaluated shortly after we assess the results.

By committing to your Food Plan forever you move your critical food decisions from your emotions and impulses to your intellect. What you are truly committing to is making intellectual food decisions about any trigger foods and/or situations from now until the day the universe ends, thereby relegating your emotional impulses and desires for food to a submissive position. You are 100% committing to follow your Food Plan forever, even if you should decide to change the Food Rules within your Food Plan at a later date.

Because the Pig's only hope is to get you to act on impulse or emotion, making a permanent shift to your intellect for these decisions is a life sentence for your Pig. When you make your commitment, your Pig will therefore show you it's entire hand. It will make one last valiant, no-holds-barred effort to convince you to change your mind.

In other words, your Pig often keeps one or two Squeals a secret during the exercises in section 3 above, hoping to surprise you with them at a later date and catch you off guard. We need to expose those Squeals and dispute them too in order to bridge the gap between whatever confidence level you're at right now and 100%!

Once that's done you probably still won't FEEL 100% confident, but you won't be able to say why. That's OK, that's called the "inescapable void" and I'll show you how to deal with it in the next section. For now, let's just force the Pig's hand and deal with whatever Squeals it may still be hiding.

Exercise 4A) Re-write the final version of your One Simple Rule below. This will comprise your entire Food Plan at first. Then put your hand over your heart, take a deep breath, and recite the following words out loud: "I will never break my Food Plan again!"

➔ **RE-WRITE YOUR ONE SIMPLE RULE HERE:** *(From Exercise 1A, 1B, or 1C, whichever is your final version.)*

_____

_____

_____

_____

_____

_____

➔ **PUT YOUR HAND OVER YOUR HEART, TAKE A DEEP BREATH, AND SAY "I WILL NEVER BREAK MY FOOD PLAN AGAIN!"** Write this statement in the space below after you've done so. *(Literally write the words in quotes).* As the meaning of this takes hold in your heart, take several more deep breaths and repeat the words several more times, each time a little louder. That should get your Pig's attention!

_____

_____

_____

_____

_____

_____

Exercise 4B). Pause for a moment to see if your Pig starts Squealing again. Is your Pig Squealing? *(Circle YES or NO below.)*

→ **YES:** OK, your Pig wants to make some more noise. No big deal. The question is, is it saying anything new which you haven't yet put in your comprehensive list of Squeals from Exercise 3A?

» **OLD SQUEALS:** If the Squeals are nothing new just then re-read the answers/disputations for these Squeals again until these Squeals aren't bothering you anymore.

» **NEW SQUEALS:** If it IS saying something new then add the new Squeal to your list from Exercise 3A and go through the same process to discover the logical distortion within each new Squeal and disempower it. Make sure to buzz through the list of Common Squeals to see if there's an existing, effective disputation you can use! Do this until ALL the new Squeals have been dealt with to the best of your ability.

→ **NO:** OK, great. Go on to Exercise 4C below.

Exercise 4C) If we define Binging as breaking your Food Plan, and if you know this first time through that you will re-evaluate your Food Plan *(comprised—at first—solely of your One Simple Rule)* **in just 10 days, how confident are you that you will NEVER Binge again?** *(Enter a number from 0% to 100% where 100% means you are absolutely, completely confident you will Never Binge Again and 0% means you'll probably Binge in about five seconds)*

→ **(i) How confident are you that you will NEVER Binge again?**

_____ *(Enter percentage here)*

→ **(ii) If you did NOT enter 100% above (most people will not at first), why not? Can you hear your Pig Squealing about anything else? If so, the question again is, is it saying anything NEW?** We follow the same procedure as we did in 4B above, repeated below for your convenience:

» **OLD SQUEALS:** If the Squeals are nothing new just then re-read the answers/disputations for these Squeals again until these Squeals aren't bothering you anymore. Then ask yourself the same question

» **NEW SQUEALS:** If it IS saying something new then add the new Squeal to your list from Exercise 3A and go through the same process to discover the logical distortion within the new Squeal and disempower it. Make sure to buzz through the list of Common Squeals to see if there's an existing, effective disputation you can use!

➔ **(iii) If you entered 100% above—OR—you entered less than 100% but cannot hear ANY new Squeals—in other words you are less than 100% confident that you will never binge again but you can't say why—go on to "Crossing the Inescapable Void with a Leap of Faith."**

➔ **(iv) If you entered less than 100% above and you DID hear a new Squeal, then return to the first question in this exercise**. Your answer should have gone up a little bit. Cross out the old number and write in the new. Repeat this exercise until your answer to 4Ciii (immediately above) takes you to "Crossing the Inescapable Void with a Leap of Faith"

Chapter 5

Achieving 100% Confidence!

If you've arrived here, you've declared your 100% commitment to at least one simple food rule, thereby creating a Food Plan. You have also gotten all your Pig's Squeals on the table and successfully disputed them. But you may not be FEELING 100% confident that you will never binge again. In fact, most people retain some residual anxiety at this juncture, but they can't quite say why.

The reason for this residual anxiety is that the Pig is comprised of a constellation of memories and old, very well-worn neurological pathways to your previous overeating behavior. You know this. Your Pig knows this. So you feel nervous. Moreover, we can't eliminate the source of your Pig's energy—the feast & famine and fight or flight survival drives in the Lizard Brain—because YOU need this energy source to survive too.

We call this place the "inescapable void" and most people get stuck here because they are unwittingly falling for one last subtle Pig Squeal they fail to recognize. That Squeal says "You need to FEEL 100% confident in order to DECLARE yourself 100% confident you will never binge again."

But that Squeal ignores the fundamental principle of Never Binge Again: Feelings are secondary and must always be subjugated to the will of your higher self. It doesn't matter how you feel. It matters how you've intellectually evaluated the best course of action for yourself.

IN NEVER BINGE AGAIN WE HAVE DISCOVERED THROUGH CAREFUL INTELLECTUAL EVALUATION THAT WHILE WE MAY NEVER FEEL 100% CONFIDENT, WE CAN STILL DECLARE OURSELVES 100% CONFIDENT THAT WE WILL NEVER BINGE AGAIN, EVEN IF OUR PIG HAS OTHER IDEAS!

In this way we can take a leap of faith to move our food decisions from our emotions and impulses to our intellect. And in so doing we have 100% committed to separating ourselves from the Pig. From now on ANY thought, feeling, emotion, impulse, and/or image which suggests we will ever break our Food Plan again IS the Pig. From now on you will translate "I'm afraid I might Binge" or "I'm afraid the Pig is going to get me to change my mind" to "The Pig really, really wants to Binge!"

Get it?

YOU have zero doubts or insecurities about breaking your Food Plan, your Pig has other thoughts entirely.

That's OK because YOU are superior to the Pig. You are neurologically wired to be its boss. You're set up to win. YOU are the alpha wolf in this pack and it's about time your Pig started to respect that.

DO NOT WAIT TO FEEL 100% CONFIDENT YOU WILL NEVER BINGE AGAIN. DECLARE YOURSELF 100% CONFIDENT AND LET THE PIG SQUEAL ITS HEAD OFF!

I know this feels weird. Every bone in your body says "wait, wait, so I'm supposed to lie to myself even if I don't feel 100% confident?"

But if you accept this thought you're failing to separate from your Pig. The essence of Never Binge Again is the commitment to this separation. We can't ever cut the Pig out of our brains, but we CAN separate our human identity from it.

The Pig is NOT some rejected part of yourself that you need to re-integrate. It's not a wounded inner child you need to find a way to love. It's NOT something which has ever served you, it's only derailed your best laid plans time and again, thereby crushing your hopes and dreams. By waiting to FEEL 100% confident you are playing by the Pig's principle. The Pig thinks that feelings are gold and must always be honored, you see. Feel like eating a donut? The Pig says you've got to do it. Feeling sad? Some chocolate and pizza is in order.

The Pig says FEELINGS come first in food decisions, but YOU say your intellect reigns supreme from now on.

"I'm 100% confident I will never binge again, but my Pig has other ideas."

That's the magic line.

Are you willing to embrace it? Are you willing to tear yourself apart from your Pig and build a success identity from here on in? Are you ready to start your new life?

Exercise 5A) Write the magic words "I'm 100% confident I will never binge again, but my Pig has other ideas" in the space below, then say them out loud three times for emphasis.

Feels good, doesn't it?

Chapter 6

Confronting the Lizard Brain in Real Time

To this point we've been building the rational thinking and motivation required to identify and disempower your Lizard's Brain's excuses and limiting beliefs. We've handed you some extremely powerful tools for separating your constructive vs. destructive thinking about food and showed you how to use them. However, everything so far has been in the war planning room, not the battlefield!

The real test comes when you're in real time facing your Pig's best ideas for overeating, and the BEST way to manage this is to call the Pig out in the moment. How does this work?

→ If your Pig has a craving you clearly recognize as the Pig, and which you feel perfectly comfortable ignoring, then simply go on with your day and leave the Pig in its Cage. After all, you know what it's up to, you know where ALL the Pig's thoughts lead, and you swore a solemn oath never to take it there again. So why give it any more attention!?

→ However, if the Pig has a craving you are TEMPTED to indulge, you'll want to call out the Pig in REAL TIME and engage it in a conversation. The idea is to get the Pig's complete and specific Squeal on the table so you can logically disempower it. You want to expose the Pig's lies in real time.

For example, in recent years the only food off plan I've had any significant trouble with is rice and beans. Many people consider rice and beans a very healthy way to eat, but I have a genetic condition which requires I abstain or else put up with moderately uncomfortable symptoms *(tremors.)* However, after a big workout, and sometimes late in the afternoon even when I haven't exercised but just got a little lazy about managing my blood sugar, my Pig generates a very strong craving.

Before I understood the principle of real-time disputation, I sometimes found myself in an "automatic" behavior chain which involved driving to a nearby health food store with a hot bar that had my favorite rice and beans all cooked, flavored and ready. Of course, the rest of the behavior chain involved turning off the car, taking my keys, opening the car door, closing it, walking into the store, going to the hot bar, picking up a container, walking to the section of the bar which had my rice and scooping it into the container, then over to the section which had the beans and scooping them similarly, going to get a lid for the container, closing it, walking over and placing the container on the scale, agreeing to the price the checkout woman told me, opening my wallet, taking out the money or a credit card, handing it to the woman, waiting for my change, putting the change in my pocket or the tip jar, answering the nice cashier's question about whether or not I needed a bag, picking up a fork and some napkins, walking to my car, opening the door, sitting down, starting the car, turning on the air conditioner *(I live in South Florida)*, putting on my seatbelt, deciding what music, news, and/

or podcasts or audible book I wanted to listen to while I ate, taking the container out of the bag, picking up the fork, opening the container, putting the first bite on my fork, putting it in my mouth, chewing, and swallowing. Then, of course, I repeat that bite 48+ times to finish the container.

Please note that ANY point along the behavior chain up until the very first bite is an opportunity to intervene with a real-time disputation, stop the train, and prevent the Binge! In fact, even after the first bite, every subsequent bite is also an opportunity. *(I went through every detail of the behavior chain above so you'd see how many decisions and behaviors are actually involved in something that feels "automatic.")*

Now that I understand real-time disputation, at the first sign the craving is starting to seem like an actual possibility, I aggressively call out my Pig: "OK Pig! Now why in the world should I eat that? What's your best reason?" Then it starts Squealing very loudly, after all this is it's chance! I take out my notepad *(or use the notes application on my smart phone)* and WRITE DOWN the Squeal right there and then, followed by identifying the lie *(disputing the Pig's logic):*

→ SQUEAL: "Because it will taste great!"

  » DISPUTATION: Yes, it will taste great. But FEELING great is much more important!

→ SQUEAL: "Because it will be fun!"

  » DISPUTATION: It won't be fun to have the tremors. It won't be fun to lose my confidence. It won't be fun to feel like I've harmed myself with food.

→ SQUEAL: "Because you work really hard and you deserve a treat"

  » DISPUTATION: I've worked really hard so I deserve to feel healthy and enjoy my body. I could treat myself to a walk on the beach, a nap, or a phone call with a friend in the same time it will take me to procure, eat, and recover from rice and beans.

→ SQUEAL: "Because you won't gain weight if you keep it to one portion"

  » DISPUTATION: I find it very difficult to keep it to one portion, and besides, weight isn't the central issue, health is!

→ SQUEAL: "Because you're not obese anymore, so even if you gain a pound or two this week it won't matter, you can put me back later".

  » DISPUTATION: It's not about the weight, it's about my health, and I always use the present moment to be healthy!

See how it works? You already understand the disputation process from the work we did in exposing and disempowering your Pig's best excuses in Chapter 4. The only trick now is to do it in REAL TIME!

At this juncture you may say "That's great Glenn, but what if I don't WANT to do it? I mean, I want to do it now, but at the moment of temptation I never want to, I only want to listen to the Pig."

Upon reflection, you'll see that this is just another Squeal to be disputed. If you wait until you WANT to do it, or until it feels comfortable to do it...you'll be waiting forever!

When I was 15 years old, I had a big crush on a girl in high school. I went down to my Dad's office in the basement and sat by his phone trying to gather up the nerve to call her. My dad happened to walk in and asked me what I was doing. I explained I really liked this girl but I felt incredibly nervous and, as much as I wanted to go out with her, I couldn't get myself to make the call. Dad said "Glenn, if you wait until it feels comfortable, she'll probably be married." So I called.

Then I got the nerve to call others. It's NEVER felt "comfortable" to me to ask a woman out, but I do it because of the results I'm after. Otherwise I'd still be sitting in my daddy's basement.

It's the same with real-time disputations. Initially, you really won't want to do it. That's OK, do it anyway.

Sometimes the moment the craving hits, it helps to first take a series of very deep breaths, tensing up all your muscles, then letting everything go as you exhale. This helps deactivate the parasympathetic nervous system and put you more so in your logical brain. It helps wrestle control away from the Lizard Brain and the feast & famine survival response that makes binging seem inevitable.

But then DO call out your Pig. Elicit the Squeals that it's trying to seduce you with at the moment. Expose the lie they contain. Then feed yourself something HEALTHY (on your Food Plan) or nurture yourself in some other way.

You're worth it!

Exercise 6A) Real Time Disputation Instructions – Finding the Pig's Lies in the Moment Before They Have a Chance to Influence Your Behavior!

→ **Resolve to carry this workbook around with you**—*along with a pen or pencil*—and take notes as per the instructions below *in real time* whenever your Pig Squeals for some Slop. This is the superior solution, but if you're unable to do so, a simple pen and paper and/or any smartphone with a notes application will do.

→ **Set a reminder on your smartphone, computer, or by simply posting notes around your house, work, and/or in your car. The reminder should say "I HAVE 100% COMMITTED TO REAL TIME DISPUTATION!"**

→ **Before acting on the impulse to break your Food Plan or any Food Rule within it, write down exactly WHY your Pig says you should do it... in detail, and IN REAL TIME!** Make sure to write the full Squeal. For example, don't just write down "We can start tomorrow", write down the totality of what the Pig is implying: "What we eat today doesn't really count because it will be just as easy to start tomorrow. Therefore, we might as well binge our faces off today. Yippeeee!!! Let's do it now!!!"

→ **Write down the appropriate disputation.** In other words, how is the Pig lying to you? Go back and check to see if you've already found the disputation in exercise 3A. Do NOT just nod and say "OK, I know what the lie is." Write it again into the template you are using (see following pages). Writing engages the upper brain more so than simply reading – and in so doing disempowers the Lizard Brain even further.

→ **Ask yourself if you need some HEALTHY food which would be compliant with your Food Rules, or perhaps you need a self-care break of some sort if remotely possible.** Write that down too so you can see patterns over time.

→ **Write down how it feels to have put the Pig in its Cage despite the craving**!

→ **Go on with your day free of Pig Slop**!

(Real Time Disputation Templates Begin on Next Page)

REAL TIME DISPUTATION TEMPLATE

What, specifically, does your Pig want you to eat and/or do which would be a violation of your current Food Plan and/or any of the Food Rules within it? *(Even just your One Simple Rule)*

_____

_____

_____

_____

_____

_____

_____

_____

How strong is this craving on a scale from one to ten, where one means "hardly worth noticing" and ten means "If I don't break my sacred Food Plan immediately I feel like I will have to put aluminum foil on my head, climb a clock tower, and scream at the top of my lungs for hours!" _____ (ENTER NUMBER)

Where is the lie in what the Pig is saying? Reference Chapter 3 for solutions to its logical distortions. *(Even just your One Simple Rule)*

_____

_____

_____

_____

_____

_____

_____

_____

What might I eat and/or do instead of feeding the Pig? What do I genuinely need for my highest and best healthy self?

_____

_____

_____

_____

_____

_____

_____

_____

_____

How does it feel to have Caged the Pig despite its craving? Be detailed please. *(HINT: It feels great! Make a mental note of what this feels like to reinforce doing the exercise every time the Squeals hit. Before you know it the Pig will (mostly) shut up!)*

_____

_____

_____

_____

_____

_____

_____

_____

REAL TIME DISPUTATION TEMPLATE

What, specifically, does your Pig want you to eat and/or do which would be a violation of your current Food Plan and/or any of the Food Rules within it? *(Even just your One Simple Rule)*

_____

_____

_____

_____

_____

_____

_____

_____

How strong is this craving on a scale from one to ten, where one means "hardly worth noticing" and ten means "If I don't break my sacred Food Plan immediately I feel like I will have to put aluminum foil on my head, climb a clock tower, and scream at the top of my lungs for hours!" _____ (ENTER NUMBER)

Where is the lie in what the Pig is saying? Reference Chapter 3 for solutions to its logical distortions. *(Even just your One Simple Rule)*

_____

_____

_____

_____

_____

_____

_____

_____

What might I eat and/or do instead of feeding the Pig? What do I genuinely need for my highest and best healthy self?

_____

_____

_____

_____

_____

_____

_____

_____

How does it feel to have Caged the Pig despite its craving? Be detailed please. *(HINT: It feels great! Make a mental note of what this feels like to reinforce doing the exercise every time the Squeals hit. Before you know it the Pig will (mostly) shut up!)*

_____

_____

_____

_____

_____

_____

_____

REAL TIME DISPUTATION TEMPLATE

What, specifically, does your Pig want you to eat and/or do which would be a violation of your current Food Plan and/or any of the Food Rules within it? *(Even just your One Simple Rule)*

_____

_____

_____

_____

_____

_____

_____

_____

How strong is this craving on a scale from one to ten, where one means "hardly worth noticing" and ten means "If I don't break my sacred Food Plan immediately I feel like I will have to put aluminum foil on my head, climb a clock tower, and scream at the top of my lungs for hours!" _____ (ENTER NUMBER)

Where is the lie in what the Pig is saying? Reference Chapter 3 for solutions to its logical distortions. *(Even just your One Simple Rule)*

_____

_____

_____

_____

_____

_____

_____

_____

What might I eat and/or do instead of feeding the Pig? What do I genuinely need for my highest and best healthy self?

_____

_____

_____

_____

_____

_____

_____

_____

How does it feel to have Caged the Pig despite its craving? Be detailed please. *(HINT: It feels great! Make a mental note of what this feels like to reinforce doing the exercise every time the Squeals hit. Before you know it the Pig will (mostly) shut up!)*

_____

_____

_____

_____

_____

_____

_____

_____

REAL TIME DISPUTATION TEMPLATE

What, specifically, does your Pig want you to eat and/or do which would be a violation of your current Food Plan and/or any of the Food Rules within it? *(Even just your One Simple Rule)*

_____

_____

_____

_____

_____

_____

_____

How strong is this craving on a scale from one to ten, where one means "hardly worth noticing" and ten means "If I don't break my sacred Food Plan immediately I feel like I will have to put aluminum foil on my head, climb a clock tower, and scream at the top of my lungs for hours!" _____ (ENTER NUMBER)

Where is the lie in what the Pig is saying? Reference Chapter 3 for solutions to its logical distortions. *(Even just your One Simple Rule)*

_____

_____

_____

_____

_____

_____

_____

What might I eat and/or do instead of feeding the Pig? What do I genuinely need for my highest and best healthy self?

_____

_____

_____

_____

_____

_____

_____

_____

How does it feel to have Caged the Pig despite its craving? Be detailed please. *(HINT: It feels great! Make a mental note of what this feels like to reinforce doing the exercise every time the Squeals hit. Before you know it the Pig will (mostly) shut up!)*

_____

_____

_____

_____

_____

_____

_____

_____

REAL TIME DISPUTATION TEMPLATE

What, specifically, does your Pig want you to eat and/or do which would be a violation of your current Food Plan and/or any of the Food Rules within it? *(Even just your One Simple Rule)*

_____

_____

_____

_____

_____

_____

_____

_____

How strong is this craving on a scale from one to ten, where one means "hardly worth noticing" and ten means "If I don't break my sacred Food Plan immediately I feel like I will have to put aluminum foil on my head, climb a clock tower, and scream at the top of my lungs for hours!" _____ (ENTER NUMBER)

Where is the lie in what the Pig is saying? Reference Chapter 3 for solutions to its logical distortions. *(Even just your One Simple Rule)*

_____

_____

_____

_____

_____

_____

_____

_____

What might I eat and/or do instead of feeding the Pig? What do I genuinely need for my highest and best healthy self?

_____
_____
_____
_____
_____
_____
_____
_____

How does it feel to have Caged the Pig despite its craving? Be detailed please. *(HINT: It feels great! Make a mental note of what this feels like to reinforce doing the exercise every time the Squeals hit. Before you know it the Pig will (mostly) shut up!)*

_____
_____
_____
_____
_____
_____
_____
_____

REAL TIME DISPUTATION TEMPLATE

What, specifically, does your Pig want you to eat and/or do which would be a violation of your current Food Plan and/or any of the Food Rules within it? *(Even just your One Simple Rule)*

_____

_____

_____

_____

_____

_____

_____

_____

How strong is this craving on a scale from one to ten, where one means "hardly worth noticing" and ten means "If I don't break my sacred Food Plan immediately I feel like I will have to put aluminum foil on my head, climb a clock tower, and scream at the top of my lungs for hours!" _____ (ENTER NUMBER)

Where is the lie in what the Pig is saying? Reference Chapter 3 for solutions to its logical distortions. *(Even just your One Simple Rule)*

_____

_____

_____

_____

_____

_____

_____

_____

What might I eat and/or do instead of feeding the Pig? What do I genuinely need for my highest and best healthy self?

_____
_____
_____
_____
_____
_____
_____
_____

How does it feel to have Caged the Pig despite its craving? Be detailed please. *(HINT: It feels great! Make a mental note of what this feels like to reinforce doing the exercise every time the Squeals hit. Before you know it the Pig will (mostly) shut up!)*

_____
_____
_____
_____
_____
_____
_____

REAL TIME DISPUTATION TEMPLATE

What, specifically, does your Pig want you to eat and/or do which would be a violation of your current Food Plan and/or any of the Food Rules within it? *(Even just your One Simple Rule)*

_____

_____

_____

_____

_____

_____

_____

_____

How strong is this craving on a scale from one to ten, where one means "hardly worth noticing" and ten means "If I don't break my sacred Food Plan immediately I feel like I will have to put aluminum foil on my head, climb a clock tower, and scream at the top of my lungs for hours!" _____ (ENTER NUMBER)

Where is the lie in what the Pig is saying? Reference Chapter 3 for solutions to its logical distortions. *(Even just your One Simple Rule)*

_____

_____

_____

_____

_____

_____

_____

_____

What might I eat and/or do instead of feeding the Pig? What do I genuinely need for my highest and best healthy self?

_____

_____

_____

_____

_____

_____

_____

_____

How does it feel to have Caged the Pig despite its craving? Be detailed please. *(HINT: It feels great! Make a mental note of what this feels like to reinforce doing the exercise every time the Squeals hit. Before you know it the Pig will (mostly) shut up!)*

_____

_____

_____

_____

_____

_____

_____

_____

REAL TIME DISPUTATION TEMPLATE

What, specifically, does your Pig want you to eat and/or do which would be a violation of your current Food Plan and/or any of the Food Rules within it? *(Even just your One Simple Rule)*

_____

_____

_____

_____

_____

_____

_____

How strong is this craving on a scale from one to ten, where one means "hardly worth noticing" and ten means "If I don't break my sacred Food Plan immediately I feel like I will have to put aluminum foil on my head, climb a clock tower, and scream at the top of my lungs for hours!" _____ (ENTER NUMBER)

Where is the lie in what the Pig is saying? Reference Chapter 3 for solutions to its logical distortions. *(Even just your One Simple Rule)*

_____

_____

_____

_____

_____

_____

_____

What might I eat and/or do instead of feeding the Pig? What do I genuinely need for my highest and best healthy self?

_____

_____

_____

_____

_____

_____

_____

_____

How does it feel to have Caged the Pig despite its craving? Be detailed please. *(HINT: It feels great! Make a mental note of what this feels like to reinforce doing the exercise every time the Squeals hit. Before you know it the Pig will (mostly) shut up!)*

_____

_____

_____

_____

_____

_____

_____

_____

REAL TIME DISPUTATION TEMPLATE

What, specifically, does your Pig want you to eat and/or do which would be a violation of your current Food Plan and/or any of the Food Rules within it? *(Even just your One Simple Rule)*

_____

_____

_____

_____

_____

_____

_____

_____

How strong is this craving on a scale from one to ten, where one means "hardly worth noticing" and ten means "If I don't break my sacred Food Plan immediately I feel like I will have to put aluminum foil on my head, climb a clock tower, and scream at the top of my lungs for hours!" _____ (ENTER NUMBER)

Where is the lie in what the Pig is saying? Reference Chapter 3 for solutions to its logical distortions. *(Even just your One Simple Rule)*

_____

_____

_____

_____

_____

_____

_____

_____

What might I eat and/or do instead of feeding the Pig? What do I genuinely need for my highest and best healthy self?

_____

_____

_____

_____

_____

_____

_____

_____

How does it feel to have Caged the Pig despite its craving? Be detailed please. *(HINT: It feels great! Make a mental note of what this feels like to reinforce doing the exercise every time the Squeals hit. Before you know it the Pig will (mostly) shut up!)*

_____

_____

_____

_____

_____

_____

_____

REAL TIME DISPUTATION TEMPLATE

What, specifically, does your Pig want you to eat and/or do which would be a violation of your current Food Plan and/or any of the Food Rules within it? *(Even just your One Simple Rule)*

_____

_____

_____

_____

_____

_____

_____

_____

_____

How strong is this craving on a scale from one to ten, where one means "hardly worth noticing" and ten means "If I don't break my sacred Food Plan immediately I feel like I will have to put aluminum foil on my head, climb a clock tower, and scream at the top of my lungs for hours!" _____ (ENTER NUMBER)

Where is the lie in what the Pig is saying? Reference Chapter 3 for solutions to its logical distortions. *(Even just your One Simple Rule)*

_____

_____

_____

_____

_____

_____

_____

_____

What might I eat and/or do instead of feeding the Pig? What do I genuinely need for my highest and best healthy self?

_____
_____
_____
_____
_____
_____
_____
_____

How does it feel to have Caged the Pig despite its craving? Be detailed please. *(HINT: It feels great! Make a mental note of what this feels like to reinforce doing the exercise every time the Squeals hit. Before you know it the Pig will (mostly) shut up!)*

_____
_____
_____
_____
_____
_____
_____
_____

REAL TIME DISPUTATION TEMPLATE

What, specifically, does your Pig want you to eat and/or do which would be a violation of your current Food Plan and/or any of the Food Rules within it? *(Even just your One Simple Rule)*

_____

_____

_____

_____

_____

_____

_____

_____

How strong is this craving on a scale from one to ten, where one means "hardly worth noticing" and ten means "If I don't break my sacred Food Plan immediately I feel like I will have to put aluminum foil on my head, climb a clock tower, and scream at the top of my lungs for hours!" _____ (ENTER NUMBER)

Where is the lie in what the Pig is saying? Reference Chapter 3 for solutions to its logical distortions. *(Even just your One Simple Rule)*

_____

_____

_____

_____

_____

_____

_____

_____

What might I eat and/or do instead of feeding the Pig? What do I genuinely need for my highest and best healthy self?

_____

_____

_____

_____

_____

_____

_____

_____

How does it feel to have Caged the Pig despite its craving? Be detailed please. *(HINT: It feels great! Make a mental note of what this feels like to reinforce doing the exercise every time the Squeals hit. Before you know it the Pig will (mostly) shut up!)*

_____

_____

_____

_____

_____

_____

_____

REAL TIME DISPUTATION TEMPLATE

What, specifically, does your Pig want you to eat and/or do which would be a violation of your current Food Plan and/or any of the Food Rules within it? *(Even just your One Simple Rule)*

How strong is this craving on a scale from one to ten, where one means "hardly worth noticing" and ten means "If I don't break my sacred Food Plan immediately I feel like I will have to put aluminum foil on my head, climb a clock tower, and scream at the top of my lungs for hours!" _____ (ENTER NUMBER)

Where is the lie in what the Pig is saying? Reference Chapter 3 for solutions to its logical distortions. *(Even just your One Simple Rule)*

What might I eat and/or do instead of feeding the Pig? What do I genuinely need for my highest and best healthy self?

How does it feel to have Caged the Pig despite its craving? Be detailed please. *(HINT: It feels great! Make a mental note of what this feels like to reinforce doing the exercise every time the Squeals hit. Before you know it the Pig will (mostly) shut up!)*

REAL TIME DISPUTATION TEMPLATE

What, specifically, does your Pig want you to eat and/or do which would be a violation of your current Food Plan and/or any of the Food Rules within it? *(Even just your One Simple Rule)*

_____

_____

_____

_____

_____

_____

_____

How strong is this craving on a scale from one to ten, where one means "hardly worth noticing" and ten means "If I don't break my sacred Food Plan immediately I feel like I will have to put aluminum foil on my head, climb a clock tower, and scream at the top of my lungs for hours!" _____ (ENTER NUMBER)

Where is the lie in what the Pig is saying? Reference Chapter 3 for solutions to its logical distortions. *(Even just your One Simple Rule)*

_____

_____

_____

_____

_____

_____

_____

_____

What might I eat and/or do instead of feeding the Pig? What do I genuinely need for my highest and best healthy self?

_____
_____
_____
_____
_____
_____
_____
_____

How does it feel to have Caged the Pig despite its craving? Be detailed please. *(HINT: It feels great! Make a mental note of what this feels like to reinforce doing the exercise every time the Squeals hit. Before you know it the Pig will (mostly) shut up!)*

_____
_____
_____
_____
_____
_____
_____

REAL TIME DISPUTATION TEMPLATE

What, specifically, does your Pig want you to eat and/or do which would be a violation of your current Food Plan and/or any of the Food Rules within it? *(Even just your One Simple Rule)*

_____

_____

_____

_____

_____

_____

_____

_____

How strong is this craving on a scale from one to ten, where one means "hardly worth noticing" and ten means "If I don't break my sacred Food Plan immediately I feel like I will have to put aluminum foil on my head, climb a clock tower, and scream at the top of my lungs for hours!" _____ (ENTER NUMBER)

Where is the lie in what the Pig is saying? Reference Chapter 3 for solutions to its logical distortions. *(Even just your One Simple Rule)*

_____

_____

_____

_____

_____

_____

_____

_____

142

What might I eat and/or do instead of feeding the Pig? What do I genuinely need for my highest and best healthy self?

_____

_____

_____

_____

_____

_____

_____

_____

How does it feel to have Caged the Pig despite its craving? Be detailed please. *(HINT: It feels great! Make a mental note of what this feels like to reinforce doing the exercise every time the Squeals hit. Before you know it the Pig will (mostly) shut up!)*

_____

_____

_____

_____

_____

_____

_____

_____

REAL TIME DISPUTATION TEMPLATE

What, specifically, does your Pig want you to eat and/or do which would be a violation of your current Food Plan and/or any of the Food Rules within it? *(Even just your One Simple Rule)*

_____

_____

_____

_____

_____

_____

_____

How strong is this craving on a scale from one to ten, where one means "hardly worth noticing" and ten means "If I don't break my sacred Food Plan immediately I feel like I will have to put aluminum foil on my head, climb a clock tower, and scream at the top of my lungs for hours!" _____ (ENTER NUMBER)

Where is the lie in what the Pig is saying? Reference Chapter 3 for solutions to its logical distortions. *(Even just your One Simple Rule)*

_____

_____

_____

_____

_____

_____

_____

What might I eat and/or do instead of feeding the Pig? What do I genuinely need for my highest and best healthy self?

_____
_____
_____
_____
_____
_____
_____
_____

How does it feel to have Caged the Pig despite its craving? Be detailed please. *(HINT: It feels great! Make a mental note of what this feels like to reinforce doing the exercise every time the Squeals hit. Before you know it the Pig will (mostly) shut up!)*

_____
_____
_____
_____
_____
_____
_____
_____

REAL TIME DISPUTATION TEMPLATE

What, specifically, does your Pig want you to eat and/or do which would be a violation of your current Food Plan and/or any of the Food Rules within it? *(Even just your One Simple Rule)*

_____

_____

_____

_____

_____

_____

_____

_____

How strong is this craving on a scale from one to ten, where one means "hardly worth noticing" and ten means "If I don't break my sacred Food Plan immediately I feel like I will have to put aluminum foil on my head, climb a clock tower, and scream at the top of my lungs for hours!" _____ (ENTER NUMBER)

Where is the lie in what the Pig is saying? Reference Chapter 3 for solutions to its logical distortions. *(Even just your One Simple Rule)*

_____

_____

_____

_____

_____

_____

_____

_____

What might I eat and/or do instead of feeding the Pig? What do I genuinely need for my highest and best healthy self?

_____

_____

_____

_____

_____

_____

_____

_____

How does it feel to have Caged the Pig despite its craving? Be detailed please. *(HINT: It feels great! Make a mental note of what this feels like to reinforce doing the exercise every time the Squeals hit. Before you know it the Pig will (mostly) shut up!)*

_____

_____

_____

_____

_____

_____

_____

_____

The Never Binge Again *Workbook*

REAL TIME DISPUTATION TEMPLATE

What, specifically, does your Pig want you to eat and/or do which would be a violation of your current Food Plan and/or any of the Food Rules within it? *(Even just your One Simple Rule)*

How strong is this craving on a scale from one to ten, where one means "hardly worth noticing" and ten means "If I don't break my sacred Food Plan immediately I feel like I will have to put aluminum foil on my head, climb a clock tower, and scream at the top of my lungs for hours!" _____ (ENTER NUMBER)

Where is the lie in what the Pig is saying? Reference Chapter 3 for solutions to its logical distortions. *(Even just your One Simple Rule)*

148

What might I eat and/or do instead of feeding the Pig? What do I genuinely need for my highest and best healthy self?

_____

_____

_____

_____

_____

_____

_____

_____

_____

How does it feel to have Caged the Pig despite its craving? Be detailed please. *(HINT: It feels great! Make a mental note of what this feels like to reinforce doing the exercise every time the Squeals hit. Before you know it the Pig will (mostly) shut up!)*

_____

_____

_____

_____

_____

_____

_____

_____

REAL TIME DISPUTATION TEMPLATE

What, specifically, does your Pig want you to eat and/or do which would be a violation of your current Food Plan and/or any of the Food Rules within it? *(Even just your One Simple Rule)*

How strong is this craving on a scale from one to ten, where one means "hardly worth noticing" and ten means "If I don't break my sacred Food Plan immediately I feel like I will have to put aluminum foil on my head, climb a clock tower, and scream at the top of my lungs for hours!" _____ (ENTER NUMBER)

Where is the lie in what the Pig is saying? Reference Chapter 3 for solutions to its logical distortions. *(Even just your One Simple Rule)*

What might I eat and/or do instead of feeding the Pig? What do I genuinely need for my highest and best healthy self?

_____

_____

_____

_____

_____

_____

_____

_____

How does it feel to have Caged the Pig despite its craving? Be detailed please. *(HINT: It feels great! Make a mental note of what this feels like to reinforce doing the exercise every time the Squeals hit. Before you know it the Pig will (mostly) shut up!)*

_____

_____

_____

_____

_____

_____

_____

REAL TIME DISPUTATION TEMPLATE

What, specifically, does your Pig want you to eat and/or do which would be a violation of your current Food Plan and/or any of the Food Rules within it? *(Even just your One Simple Rule)*

_____

_____

_____

_____

_____

_____

_____

_____

_____

How strong is this craving on a scale from one to ten, where one means "hardly worth noticing" and ten means "If I don't break my sacred Food Plan immediately I feel like I will have to put aluminum foil on my head, climb a clock tower, and scream at the top of my lungs for hours!" _____ (ENTER NUMBER)

Where is the lie in what the Pig is saying? Reference Chapter 3 for solutions to its logical distortions. *(Even just your One Simple Rule)*

_____

_____

_____

_____

_____

_____

_____

_____

_____

What might I eat and/or do instead of feeding the Pig? What do I genuinely need for my highest and best healthy self?

_____
_____
_____
_____
_____
_____
_____
_____

How does it feel to have Caged the Pig despite its craving? Be detailed please. *(HINT: It feels great! Make a mental note of what this feels like to reinforce doing the exercise every time the Squeals hit. Before you know it the Pig will (mostly) shut up!)*

_____
_____
_____
_____
_____
_____
_____
_____

REAL TIME DISPUTATION TEMPLATE

What, specifically, does your Pig want you to eat and/or do which would be a violation of your current Food Plan and/or any of the Food Rules within it? *(Even just your One Simple Rule)*

_____

_____

_____

_____

_____

_____

_____

_____

_____

How strong is this craving on a scale from one to ten, where one means "hardly worth noticing" and ten means "If I don't break my sacred Food Plan immediately I feel like I will have to put aluminum foil on my head, climb a clock tower, and scream at the top of my lungs for hours!" _____ (ENTER NUMBER)

Where is the lie in what the Pig is saying? Reference Chapter 3 for solutions to its logical distortions. *(Even just your One Simple Rule)*

_____

_____

_____

_____

_____

_____

_____

_____

_____

What might I eat and/or do instead of feeding the Pig? What do I genuinely need for my highest and best healthy self?

_____

_____

_____

_____

_____

_____

_____

_____

How does it feel to have Caged the Pig despite its craving? Be detailed please. *(HINT: It feels great! Make a mental note of what this feels like to reinforce doing the exercise every time the Squeals hit. Before you know it the Pig will (mostly) shut up!)*

_____

_____

_____

_____

_____

_____

_____

REAL TIME DISPUTATION TEMPLATE

What, specifically, does your Pig want you to eat and/or do which would be a violation of your current Food Plan and/or any of the Food Rules within it? *(Even just your One Simple Rule)*

_____

_____

_____

_____

_____

_____

_____

How strong is this craving on a scale from one to ten, where one means "hardly worth noticing" and ten means "If I don't break my sacred Food Plan immediately I feel like I will have to put aluminum foil on my head, climb a clock tower, and scream at the top of my lungs for hours!" _____ (ENTER NUMBER)

Where is the lie in what the Pig is saying? Reference Chapter 3 for solutions to its logical distortions. *(Even just your One Simple Rule)*

_____

_____

_____

_____

_____

_____

_____

_____

What might I eat and/or do instead of feeding the Pig? What do I genuinely need for my highest and best healthy self?

_____

_____

_____

_____

_____

_____

_____

_____

How does it feel to have Caged the Pig despite its craving? Be detailed please. *(HINT: It feels great! Make a mental note of what this feels like to reinforce doing the exercise every time the Squeals hit. Before you know it the Pig will (mostly) shut up!)*

_____

_____

_____

_____

_____

_____

_____

_____

REAL TIME DISPUTATION TEMPLATE

What, specifically, does your Pig want you to eat and/or do which would be a violation of your current Food Plan and/or any of the Food Rules within it? *(Even just your One Simple Rule)*

_____

_____

_____

_____

_____

_____

_____

How strong is this craving on a scale from one to ten, where one means "hardly worth noticing" and ten means "If I don't break my sacred Food Plan immediately I feel like I will have to put aluminum foil on my head, climb a clock tower, and scream at the top of my lungs for hours!" _____ (ENTER NUMBER)

Where is the lie in what the Pig is saying? Reference Chapter 3 for solutions to its logical distortions. *(Even just your One Simple Rule)*

_____

_____

_____

_____

_____

_____

_____

What might I eat and/or do instead of feeding the Pig? What do I genuinely need for my highest and best healthy self?

_____

_____

_____

_____

_____

_____

_____

_____

How does it feel to have Caged the Pig despite its craving? Be detailed please. *(HINT: It feels great! Make a mental note of what this feels like to reinforce doing the exercise every time the Squeals hit. Before you know it the Pig will (mostly) shut up!)*

_____

_____

_____

_____

_____

_____

_____

_____

REAL TIME DISPUTATION TEMPLATE

What, specifically, does your Pig want you to eat and/or do which would be a violation of your current Food Plan and/or any of the Food Rules within it? *(Even just your One Simple Rule)*

_____
_____
_____
_____
_____
_____
_____
_____

How strong is this craving on a scale from one to ten, where one means "hardly worth noticing" and ten means "If I don't break my sacred Food Plan immediately I feel like I will have to put aluminum foil on my head, climb a clock tower, and scream at the top of my lungs for hours!" _____ (ENTER NUMBER)

Where is the lie in what the Pig is saying? Reference Chapter 3 for solutions to its logical distortions. *(Even just your One Simple Rule)*

_____
_____
_____
_____
_____
_____
_____
_____

What might I eat and/or do instead of feeding the Pig? What do I genuinely need for my highest and best healthy self?

_____

_____

_____

_____

_____

_____

_____

_____

How does it feel to have Caged the Pig despite its craving? Be detailed please. *(HINT: It feels great! Make a mental note of what this feels like to reinforce doing the exercise every time the Squeals hit. Before you know it the Pig will (mostly) shut up!)*

_____

_____

_____

_____

_____

_____

_____

_____

REAL TIME DISPUTATION TEMPLATE

What, specifically, does your Pig want you to eat and/or do which would be a violation of your current Food Plan and/or any of the Food Rules within it? *(Even just your One Simple Rule)*

_____

_____

_____

_____

_____

_____

_____

How strong is this craving on a scale from one to ten, where one means "hardly worth noticing" and ten means "If I don't break my sacred Food Plan immediately I feel like I will have to put aluminum foil on my head, climb a clock tower, and scream at the top of my lungs for hours!" _____ (ENTER NUMBER)

Where is the lie in what the Pig is saying? Reference Chapter 3 for solutions to its logical distortions. *(Even just your One Simple Rule)*

_____

_____

_____

_____

_____

_____

_____

What might I eat and/or do instead of feeding the Pig? What do I genuinely need for my highest and best healthy self?

_____

_____

_____

_____

_____

_____

_____

_____

How does it feel to have Caged the Pig despite its craving? Be detailed please. *(HINT: It feels great! Make a mental note of what this feels like to reinforce doing the exercise every time the Squeals hit. Before you know it the Pig will (mostly) shut up!)*

_____

_____

_____

_____

_____

_____

_____

REAL TIME DISPUTATION TEMPLATE

What, specifically, does your Pig want you to eat and/or do which would be a violation of your current Food Plan and/or any of the Food Rules within it? *(Even just your One Simple Rule)*

_____

_____

_____

_____

_____

_____

_____

How strong is this craving on a scale from one to ten, where one means "hardly worth noticing" and ten means "If I don't break my sacred Food Plan immediately I feel like I will have to put aluminum foil on my head, climb a clock tower, and scream at the top of my lungs for hours!" _____ (ENTER NUMBER)

Where is the lie in what the Pig is saying? Reference Chapter 3 for solutions to its logical distortions. *(Even just your One Simple Rule)*

_____

_____

_____

_____

_____

_____

_____

_____

What might I eat and/or do instead of feeding the Pig? What do I genuinely need for my highest and best healthy self?

_____

_____

_____

_____

_____

_____

_____

_____

How does it feel to have Caged the Pig despite its craving? Be detailed please. *(HINT: It feels great! Make a mental note of what this feels like to reinforce doing the exercise every time the Squeals hit. Before you know it the Pig will (mostly) shut up!)*

_____

_____

_____

_____

_____

_____

_____

_____

REAL TIME DISPUTATION TEMPLATE

What, specifically, does your Pig want you to eat and/or do which would be a violation of your current Food Plan and/or any of the Food Rules within it? *(Even just your One Simple Rule)*

_____

_____

_____

_____

_____

_____

_____

How strong is this craving on a scale from one to ten, where one means "hardly worth noticing" and ten means "If I don't break my sacred Food Plan immediately I feel like I will have to put aluminum foil on my head, climb a clock tower, and scream at the top of my lungs for hours!" _____ (ENTER NUMBER)

Where is the lie in what the Pig is saying? Reference Chapter 3 for solutions to its logical distortions. *(Even just your One Simple Rule)*

_____

_____

_____

_____

_____

_____

_____

_____

What might I eat and/or do instead of feeding the Pig? What do I genuinely need for my highest and best healthy self?

_____

_____

_____

_____

_____

_____

_____

_____

How does it feel to have Caged the Pig despite its craving? Be detailed please. *(HINT: It feels great! Make a mental note of what this feels like to reinforce doing the exercise every time the Squeals hit. Before you know it the Pig will (mostly) shut up!)*

_____

_____

_____

_____

_____

_____

_____

_____

REAL TIME DISPUTATION TEMPLATE

What, specifically, does your Pig want you to eat and/or do which would be a violation of your current Food Plan and/or any of the Food Rules within it? *(Even just your One Simple Rule)*

_____

_____

_____

_____

_____

_____

_____

_____

_____

How strong is this craving on a scale from one to ten, where one means "hardly worth noticing" and ten means "If I don't break my sacred Food Plan immediately I feel like I will have to put aluminum foil on my head, climb a clock tower, and scream at the top of my lungs for hours!" _____ (ENTER NUMBER)

Where is the lie in what the Pig is saying? Reference Chapter 3 for solutions to its logical distortions. *(Even just your One Simple Rule)*

_____

_____

_____

_____

_____

_____

_____

_____

What might I eat and/or do instead of feeding the Pig? What do I genuinely need for my highest and best healthy self?

_____

_____

_____

_____

_____

_____

_____

_____

How does it feel to have Caged the Pig despite its craving? Be detailed please. *(HINT: It feels great! Make a mental note of what this feels like to reinforce doing the exercise every time the Squeals hit. Before you know it the Pig will (mostly) shut up!)*

_____

_____

_____

_____

_____

_____

_____

REAL TIME DISPUTATION TEMPLATE

What, specifically, does your Pig want you to eat and/or do which would be a violation of your current Food Plan and/or any of the Food Rules within it? *(Even just your One Simple Rule)*

_____

_____

_____

_____

_____

_____

_____

_____

How strong is this craving on a scale from one to ten, where one means "hardly worth noticing" and ten means "If I don't break my sacred Food Plan immediately I feel like I will have to put aluminum foil on my head, climb a clock tower, and scream at the top of my lungs for hours!" _____ (ENTER NUMBER)

Where is the lie in what the Pig is saying? Reference Chapter 3 for solutions to its logical distortions. *(Even just your One Simple Rule)*

_____

_____

_____

_____

_____

_____

_____

_____

What might I eat and/or do instead of feeding the Pig? What do I genuinely need for my highest and best healthy self?

_____

_____

_____

_____

_____

_____

_____

_____

How does it feel to have Caged the Pig despite its craving? Be detailed please. *(HINT: It feels great! Make a mental note of what this feels like to reinforce doing the exercise every time the Squeals hit. Before you know it the Pig will (mostly) shut up!)*

_____

_____

_____

_____

_____

_____

_____

REAL TIME DISPUTATION TEMPLATE

What, specifically, does your Pig want you to eat and/or do which would be a violation of your current Food Plan and/or any of the Food Rules within it? *(Even just your One Simple Rule)*

_____

_____

_____

_____

_____

_____

_____

How strong is this craving on a scale from one to ten, where one means "hardly worth noticing" and ten means "If I don't break my sacred Food Plan immediately I feel like I will have to put aluminum foil on my head, climb a clock tower, and scream at the top of my lungs for hours!" _____ (ENTER NUMBER)

Where is the lie in what the Pig is saying? Reference Chapter 3 for solutions to its logical distortions. *(Even just your One Simple Rule)*

_____

_____

_____

_____

_____

_____

_____

What might I eat and/or do instead of feeding the Pig? What do I genuinely need for my highest and best healthy self?

_____

_____

_____

_____

_____

_____

_____

_____

How does it feel to have Caged the Pig despite its craving? Be detailed please. *(HINT: It feels great! Make a mental note of what this feels like to reinforce doing the exercise every time the Squeals hit. Before you know it the Pig will (mostly) shut up!)*

_____

_____

_____

_____

_____

_____

_____

REAL TIME DISPUTATION TEMPLATE

What, specifically, does your Pig want you to eat and/or do which would be a violation of your current Food Plan and/or any of the Food Rules within it? *(Even just your One Simple Rule)*

_____

_____

_____

_____

_____

_____

_____

How strong is this craving on a scale from one to ten, where one means "hardly worth noticing" and ten means "If I don't break my sacred Food Plan immediately I feel like I will have to put aluminum foil on my head, climb a clock tower, and scream at the top of my lungs for hours!" _____ (ENTER NUMBER)

Where is the lie in what the Pig is saying? Reference Chapter 3 for solutions to its logical distortions. *(Even just your One Simple Rule)*

_____

_____

_____

_____

_____

_____

_____

What might I eat and/or do instead of feeding the Pig? What do I genuinely need for my highest and best healthy self?

_____

_____

_____

_____

_____

_____

_____

_____

How does it feel to have Caged the Pig despite its craving? Be detailed please. *(HINT: It feels great! Make a mental note of what this feels like to reinforce doing the exercise every time the Squeals hit. Before you know it the Pig will (mostly) shut up!)*

_____

_____

_____

_____

_____

_____

_____

REAL TIME DISPUTATION TEMPLATE

What, specifically, does your Pig want you to eat and/or do which would be a violation of your current Food Plan and/or any of the Food Rules within it? *(Even just your One Simple Rule)*

_____

_____

_____

_____

_____

_____

_____

_____

_____

How strong is this craving on a scale from one to ten, where one means "hardly worth noticing" and ten means "If I don't break my sacred Food Plan immediately I feel like I will have to put aluminum foil on my head, climb a clock tower, and scream at the top of my lungs for hours!" _____ (ENTER NUMBER)

Where is the lie in what the Pig is saying? Reference Chapter 3 for solutions to its logical distortions. *(Even just your One Simple Rule)*

_____

_____

_____

_____

_____

_____

_____

_____

_____

What might I eat and/or do instead of feeding the Pig? What do I genuinely need for my highest and best healthy self?

_____

_____

_____

_____

_____

_____

_____

How does it feel to have Caged the Pig despite its craving? Be detailed please. *(HINT: It feels great! Make a mental note of what this feels like to reinforce doing the exercise every time the Squeals hit. Before you know it the Pig will (mostly) shut up!)*

_____

_____

_____

_____

_____

_____

_____

REAL TIME DISPUTATION TEMPLATE

What, specifically, does your Pig want you to eat and/or do which would be a violation of your current Food Plan and/or any of the Food Rules within it? *(Even just your One Simple Rule)*

_____

_____

_____

_____

_____

_____

_____

How strong is this craving on a scale from one to ten, where one means "hardly worth noticing" and ten means "If I don't break my sacred Food Plan immediately I feel like I will have to put aluminum foil on my head, climb a clock tower, and scream at the top of my lungs for hours!" _____ (ENTER NUMBER)

Where is the lie in what the Pig is saying? Reference Chapter 3 for solutions to its logical distortions. *(Even just your One Simple Rule)*

_____

_____

_____

_____

_____

_____

_____

What might I eat and/or do instead of feeding the Pig? What do I genuinely need for my highest and best healthy self?

_____

_____

_____

_____

_____

_____

_____

_____

How does it feel to have Caged the Pig despite its craving? Be detailed please. *(HINT: It feels great! Make a mental note of what this feels like to reinforce doing the exercise every time the Squeals hit. Before you know it the Pig will (mostly) shut up!)*

_____

_____

_____

_____

_____

_____

_____

The Never Binge Again *Workbook*

REAL TIME DISPUTATION TEMPLATE

What, specifically, does your Pig want you to eat and/or do which would be a violation of your current Food Plan and/or any of the Food Rules within it? *(Even just your One Simple Rule)*

_____

_____

_____

_____

_____

_____

_____

_____

_____

How strong is this craving on a scale from one to ten, where one means "hardly worth noticing" and ten means "If I don't break my sacred Food Plan immediately I feel like I will have to put aluminum foil on my head, climb a clock tower, and scream at the top of my lungs for hours!" _____ (ENTER NUMBER)

Where is the lie in what the Pig is saying? Reference Chapter 3 for solutions to its logical distortions. *(Even just your One Simple Rule)*

_____

_____

_____

_____

_____

_____

_____

_____

What might I eat and/or do instead of feeding the Pig? What do I genuinely need for my highest and best healthy self?

_____

_____

_____

_____

_____

_____

_____

_____

How does it feel to have Caged the Pig despite its craving? Be detailed please. *(HINT: It feels great! Make a mental note of what this feels like to reinforce doing the exercise every time the Squeals hit. Before you know it the Pig will (mostly) shut up!)*

_____

_____

_____

_____

_____

_____

_____

_____

REAL TIME DISPUTATION TEMPLATE

What, specifically, does your Pig want you to eat and/or do which would be a violation of your current Food Plan and/or any of the Food Rules within it? *(Even just your One Simple Rule)*

_____

_____

_____

_____

_____

_____

_____

How strong is this craving on a scale from one to ten, where one means "hardly worth noticing" and ten means "If I don't break my sacred Food Plan immediately I feel like I will have to put aluminum foil on my head, climb a clock tower, and scream at the top of my lungs for hours!" _____ (ENTER NUMBER)

Where is the lie in what the Pig is saying? Reference Chapter 3 for solutions to its logical distortions. *(Even just your One Simple Rule)*

_____

_____

_____

_____

_____

_____

_____

_____

What might I eat and/or do instead of feeding the Pig? What do I genuinely need for my highest and best healthy self?

_____
_____
_____
_____
_____
_____
_____
_____

How does it feel to have Caged the Pig despite its craving? Be detailed please. *(HINT: It feels great! Make a mental note of what this feels like to reinforce doing the exercise every time the Squeals hit. Before you know it the Pig will (mostly) shut up!)*

_____
_____
_____
_____
_____
_____
_____

REAL TIME DISPUTATION TEMPLATE

What, specifically, does your Pig want you to eat and/or do which would be a violation of your current Food Plan and/or any of the Food Rules within it? *(Even just your One Simple Rule)*

_____

_____

_____

_____

_____

_____

_____

_____

_____

How strong is this craving on a scale from one to ten, where one means "hardly worth noticing" and ten means "If I don't break my sacred Food Plan immediately I feel like I will have to put aluminum foil on my head, climb a clock tower, and scream at the top of my lungs for hours!" _____ (ENTER NUMBER)

Where is the lie in what the Pig is saying? Reference Chapter 3 for solutions to its logical distortions. *(Even just your One Simple Rule)*

_____

_____

_____

_____

_____

_____

_____

_____

What might I eat and/or do instead of feeding the Pig? What do I genuinely need for my highest and best healthy self?

_____

_____

_____

_____

_____

_____

_____

_____

How does it feel to have Caged the Pig despite its craving? Be detailed please. *(HINT: It feels great! Make a mental note of what this feels like to reinforce doing the exercise every time the Squeals hit. Before you know it the Pig will (mostly) shut up!)*

_____

_____

_____

_____

_____

_____

_____

REAL TIME DISPUTATION TEMPLATE

What, specifically, does your Pig want you to eat and/or do which would be a violation of your current Food Plan and/or any of the Food Rules within it? *(Even just your One Simple Rule)*

_____

_____

_____

_____

_____

_____

_____

_____

How strong is this craving on a scale from one to ten, where one means "hardly worth noticing" and ten means "If I don't break my sacred Food Plan immediately I feel like I will have to put aluminum foil on my head, climb a clock tower, and scream at the top of my lungs for hours!" _____ (ENTER NUMBER)

Where is the lie in what the Pig is saying? Reference Chapter 3 for solutions to its logical distortions. *(Even just your One Simple Rule)*

_____

_____

_____

_____

_____

_____

_____

_____

What might I eat and/or do instead of feeding the Pig? What do I genuinely need for my highest and best healthy self?

_____
_____
_____
_____
_____
_____
_____
_____
_____

How does it feel to have Caged the Pig despite its craving? Be detailed please. *(HINT: It feels great! Make a mental note of what this feels like to reinforce doing the exercise every time the Squeals hit. Before you know it the Pig will (mostly) shut up!)*

_____
_____
_____
_____
_____
_____
_____
_____

REAL TIME DISPUTATION TEMPLATE

What, specifically, does your Pig want you to eat and/or do which would be a violation of your current Food Plan and/or any of the Food Rules within it? *(Even just your One Simple Rule)*

_____
_____
_____
_____
_____
_____
_____
_____

How strong is this craving on a scale from one to ten, where one means "hardly worth noticing" and ten means "If I don't break my sacred Food Plan immediately I feel like I will have to put aluminum foil on my head, climb a clock tower, and scream at the top of my lungs for hours!" _____ (ENTER NUMBER)

Where is the lie in what the Pig is saying? Reference Chapter 3 for solutions to its logical distortions. *(Even just your One Simple Rule)*

_____
_____
_____
_____
_____
_____
_____
_____

What might I eat and/or do instead of feeding the Pig? What do I genuinely need for my highest and best healthy self?

_____

_____

_____

_____

_____

_____

_____

How does it feel to have Caged the Pig despite its craving? Be detailed please. *(HINT: It feels great! Make a mental note of what this feels like to reinforce doing the exercise every time the Squeals hit. Before you know it the Pig will (mostly) shut up!)*

_____

_____

_____

_____

_____

_____

_____

REAL TIME DISPUTATION TEMPLATE

What, specifically, does your Pig want you to eat and/or do which would be a violation of your current Food Plan and/or any of the Food Rules within it? *(Even just your One Simple Rule)*

_____

_____

_____

_____

_____

_____

_____

How strong is this craving on a scale from one to ten, where one means "hardly worth noticing" and ten means "If I don't break my sacred Food Plan immediately I feel like I will have to put aluminum foil on my head, climb a clock tower, and scream at the top of my lungs for hours!" _____ (ENTER NUMBER)

Where is the lie in what the Pig is saying? Reference Chapter 3 for solutions to its logical distortions. *(Even just your One Simple Rule)*

_____

_____

_____

_____

_____

_____

_____

_____

What might I eat and/or do instead of feeding the Pig? What do I genuinely need for my highest and best healthy self?

_____

_____

_____

_____

_____

_____

_____

_____

How does it feel to have Caged the Pig despite its craving? Be detailed please. *(HINT: It feels great! Make a mental note of what this feels like to reinforce doing the exercise every time the Squeals hit. Before you know it the Pig will (mostly) shut up!)*

_____

_____

_____

_____

_____

_____

_____

_____

REAL TIME DISPUTATION TEMPLATE

What, specifically, does your Pig want you to eat and/or do which would be a violation of your current Food Plan and/or any of the Food Rules within it? *(Even just your One Simple Rule)*

_____

_____

_____

_____

_____

_____

_____

How strong is this craving on a scale from one to ten, where one means "hardly worth noticing" and ten means "If I don't break my sacred Food Plan immediately I feel like I will have to put aluminum foil on my head, climb a clock tower, and scream at the top of my lungs for hours!" _____ (ENTER NUMBER)

Where is the lie in what the Pig is saying? Reference Chapter 3 for solutions to its logical distortions. *(Even just your One Simple Rule)*

_____

_____

_____

_____

_____

_____

_____

What might I eat and/or do instead of feeding the Pig? What do I genuinely need for my highest and best healthy self?

_____

_____

_____

_____

_____

_____

_____

_____

How does it feel to have Caged the Pig despite its craving? Be detailed please. *(HINT: It feels great! Make a mental note of what this feels like to reinforce doing the exercise every time the Squeals hit. Before you know it the Pig will (mostly) shut up!)*

_____

_____

_____

_____

_____

_____

_____

_____

REAL TIME DISPUTATION TEMPLATE

What, specifically, does your Pig want you to eat and/or do which would be a violation of your current Food Plan and/or any of the Food Rules within it? *(Even just your One Simple Rule)*

_____

_____

_____

_____

_____

_____

_____

_____

_____

How strong is this craving on a scale from one to ten, where one means "hardly worth noticing" and ten means "If I don't break my sacred Food Plan immediately I feel like I will have to put aluminum foil on my head, climb a clock tower, and scream at the top of my lungs for hours!" _____ (ENTER NUMBER)

Where is the lie in what the Pig is saying? Reference Chapter 3 for solutions to its logical distortions. *(Even just your One Simple Rule)*

_____

_____

_____

_____

_____

_____

_____

_____

What might I eat and/or do instead of feeding the Pig? What do I genuinely need for my highest and best healthy self?

_____

_____

_____

_____

_____

_____

_____

_____

How does it feel to have Caged the Pig despite its craving? Be detailed please. *(HINT: It feels great! Make a mental note of what this feels like to reinforce doing the exercise every time the Squeals hit. Before you know it the Pig will (mostly) shut up!)*

_____

_____

_____

_____

_____

_____

_____

REAL TIME DISPUTATION TEMPLATE

What, specifically, does your Pig want you to eat and/or do which would be a violation of your current Food Plan and/or any of the Food Rules within it? *(Even just your One Simple Rule)*

_____

_____

_____

_____

_____

_____

_____

How strong is this craving on a scale from one to ten, where one means "hardly worth noticing" and ten means "If I don't break my sacred Food Plan immediately I feel like I will have to put aluminum foil on my head, climb a clock tower, and scream at the top of my lungs for hours!" _____ (ENTER NUMBER)

Where is the lie in what the Pig is saying? Reference Chapter 3 for solutions to its logical distortions. *(Even just your One Simple Rule)*

_____

_____

_____

_____

_____

_____

_____

What might I eat and/or do instead of feeding the Pig? What do I genuinely need for my highest and best healthy self?

_____

_____

_____

_____

_____

_____

_____

_____

How does it feel to have Caged the Pig despite its craving? Be detailed please. *(HINT: It feels great! Make a mental note of what this feels like to reinforce doing the exercise every time the Squeals hit. Before you know it the Pig will (mostly) shut up!)*

_____

_____

_____

_____

_____

_____

_____

_____

REAL TIME DISPUTATION TEMPLATE

What, specifically, does your Pig want you to eat and/or do which would be a violation of your current Food Plan and/or any of the Food Rules within it? *(Even just your One Simple Rule)*

_____

_____

_____

_____

_____

_____

_____

How strong is this craving on a scale from one to ten, where one means "hardly worth noticing" and ten means "If I don't break my sacred Food Plan immediately I feel like I will have to put aluminum foil on my head, climb a clock tower, and scream at the top of my lungs for hours!" _____ (ENTER NUMBER)

Where is the lie in what the Pig is saying? Reference Chapter 3 for solutions to its logical distortions. *(Even just your One Simple Rule)*

_____

_____

_____

_____

_____

_____

_____

What might I eat and/or do instead of feeding the Pig? What do I genuinely need for my highest and best healthy self?

_____

_____

_____

_____

_____

_____

_____

_____

_____

How does it feel to have Caged the Pig despite its craving? Be detailed please. *(HINT: It feels great! Make a mental note of what this feels like to reinforce doing the exercise every time the Squeals hit. Before you know it the Pig will (mostly) shut up!)*

_____

_____

_____

_____

_____

_____

_____

_____

REAL TIME DISPUTATION TEMPLATE

What, specifically, does your Pig want you to eat and/or do which would be a violation of your current Food Plan and/or any of the Food Rules within it? *(Even just your One Simple Rule)*

_____

_____

_____

_____

_____

_____

_____

_____

How strong is this craving on a scale from one to ten, where one means "hardly worth noticing" and ten means "If I don't break my sacred Food Plan immediately I feel like I will have to put aluminum foil on my head, climb a clock tower, and scream at the top of my lungs for hours!" _____ (ENTER NUMBER)

Where is the lie in what the Pig is saying? Reference Chapter 3 for solutions to its logical distortions. *(Even just your One Simple Rule)*

_____

_____

_____

_____

_____

_____

_____

_____

What might I eat and/or do instead of feeding the Pig? What do I genuinely need for my highest and best healthy self?

How does it feel to have Caged the Pig despite its craving? Be detailed please. *(HINT: It feels great! Make a mental note of what this feels like to reinforce doing the exercise every time the Squeals hit. Before you know it the Pig will (mostly) shut up!)*

REAL TIME DISPUTATION TEMPLATE

What, specifically, does your Pig want you to eat and/or do which would be a violation of your current Food Plan and/or any of the Food Rules within it? *(Even just your One Simple Rule)*

_____

_____

_____

_____

_____

_____

_____

How strong is this craving on a scale from one to ten, where one means "hardly worth noticing" and ten means "If I don't break my sacred Food Plan immediately I feel like I will have to put aluminum foil on my head, climb a clock tower, and scream at the top of my lungs for hours!" _____ (ENTER NUMBER)

Where is the lie in what the Pig is saying? Reference Chapter 3 for solutions to its logical distortions. *(Even just your One Simple Rule)*

_____

_____

_____

_____

_____

_____

_____

_____

What might I eat and/or do instead of feeding the Pig? What do I genuinely need for my highest and best healthy self?

_____

_____

_____

_____

_____

_____

_____

_____

How does it feel to have Caged the Pig despite its craving? Be detailed please. *(HINT: It feels great! Make a mental note of what this feels like to reinforce doing the exercise every time the Squeals hit. Before you know it the Pig will (mostly) shut up!)*

_____

_____

_____

_____

_____

_____

_____

REAL TIME DISPUTATION TEMPLATE

What, specifically, does your Pig want you to eat and/or do which would be a violation of your current Food Plan and/or any of the Food Rules within it? *(Even just your One Simple Rule)*

How strong is this craving on a scale from one to ten, where one means "hardly worth noticing" and ten means "If I don't break my sacred Food Plan immediately I feel like I will have to put aluminum foil on my head, climb a clock tower, and scream at the top of my lungs for hours!" _____ (ENTER NUMBER)

Where is the lie in what the Pig is saying? Reference Chapter 3 for solutions to its logical distortions. *(Even just your One Simple Rule)*

What might I eat and/or do instead of feeding the Pig? What do I genuinely need for my highest and best healthy self?

How does it feel to have Caged the Pig despite its craving? Be detailed please. *(HINT: It feels great! Make a mental note of what this feels like to reinforce doing the exercise every time the Squeals hit. Before you know it the Pig will (mostly) shut up!)*

REAL TIME DISPUTATION TEMPLATE

What, specifically, does your Pig want you to eat and/or do which would be a violation of your current Food Plan and/or any of the Food Rules within it? *(Even just your One Simple Rule)*

_____

_____

_____

_____

_____

_____

_____

_____

How strong is this craving on a scale from one to ten, where one means "hardly worth noticing" and ten means "If I don't break my sacred Food Plan immediately I feel like I will have to put aluminum foil on my head, climb a clock tower, and scream at the top of my lungs for hours!" _____ (ENTER NUMBER)

Where is the lie in what the Pig is saying? Reference Chapter 3 for solutions to its logical distortions. *(Even just your One Simple Rule)*

_____

_____

_____

_____

_____

_____

_____

_____

What might I eat and/or do instead of feeding the Pig? What do I genuinely need for my highest and best healthy self?

How does it feel to have Caged the Pig despite its craving? Be detailed please. *(HINT: It feels great! Make a mental note of what this feels like to reinforce doing the exercise every time the Squeals hit. Before you know it the Pig will (mostly) shut up!)*

REAL TIME DISPUTATION TEMPLATE

What, specifically, does your Pig want you to eat and/or do which would be a violation of your current Food Plan and/or any of the Food Rules within it? *(Even just your One Simple Rule)*

_____

_____

_____

_____

_____

_____

_____

How strong is this craving on a scale from one to ten, where one means "hardly worth noticing" and ten means "If I don't break my sacred Food Plan immediately I feel like I will have to put aluminum foil on my head, climb a clock tower, and scream at the top of my lungs for hours!" _____ (ENTER NUMBER)

Where is the lie in what the Pig is saying? Reference Chapter 3 for solutions to its logical distortions. *(Even just your One Simple Rule)*

_____

_____

_____

_____

_____

_____

_____

_____

What might I eat and/or do instead of feeding the Pig? What do I genuinely need for my highest and best healthy self?

_____

_____

_____

_____

_____

_____

_____

_____

How does it feel to have Caged the Pig despite its craving? Be detailed please. *(HINT: It feels great! Make a mental note of what this feels like to reinforce doing the exercise every time the Squeals hit. Before you know it the Pig will (mostly) shut up!)*

_____

_____

_____

_____

_____

_____

_____

REAL TIME DISPUTATION TEMPLATE

What, specifically, does your Pig want you to eat and/or do which would be a violation of your current Food Plan and/or any of the Food Rules within it? *(Even just your One Simple Rule)*

_____

_____

_____

_____

_____

_____

_____

How strong is this craving on a scale from one to ten, where one means "hardly worth noticing" and ten means "If I don't break my sacred Food Plan immediately I feel like I will have to put aluminum foil on my head, climb a clock tower, and scream at the top of my lungs for hours!" _____ (ENTER NUMBER)

Where is the lie in what the Pig is saying? Reference Chapter 3 for solutions to its logical distortions. *(Even just your One Simple Rule)*

_____

_____

_____

_____

_____

_____

_____

_____

What might I eat and/or do instead of feeding the Pig? What do I genuinely need for my highest and best healthy self?

_____

_____

_____

_____

_____

_____

_____

_____

How does it feel to have Caged the Pig despite its craving? Be detailed please. *(HINT: It feels great! Make a mental note of what this feels like to reinforce doing the exercise every time the Squeals hit. Before you know it the Pig will (mostly) shut up!)*

_____

_____

_____

_____

_____

_____

_____

Chapter 7

Noticing Your Progress

A life without binge eating and overeating feels qualitatively different than when you're "in the Slop" full force. Depending upon what rule they adopt, life slowly but surely becomes dramatically better for most people. Digestion is easier. They have progressively more energy to do other things as the days roll by. They feel more productive. They start to sleep better. Panic about overeating begins to subside. They feel more optimistic, hopeful, and enthusiastic about their life and their goals. Genuine confidence and security start to build. Sometimes people's skin starts to clear up, even in the first week or so. Relationships may start to improve. They begin to enjoy other sensations in life—how their dog's fur feels, what their children's hair smells like, a hug, etc. Breathing becomes more enjoyable. The feel of the outside air against their skin becomes noticeable. Everything changes, slowly.

Your Pig does NOT want you to take in how much better it feels to be even a little more in control, because as you notice these things, breaking your rule is going to seem progressively less attractive!

Exercise 7A) To counter the above, take just a few notes about the *positive* changes you observe every day as you follow your Food Plan *(even if it's just One Simple Rule)* for the first ten days. It's better if you can do this in real time. Take the workbook with you and take notes as you go through your day. Ideally you would also do this first thing in the morning when you arise, and last thing before you go to sleep at night, but the real-time notes are most important. I've left you some space and time cues to do so:

➔ **DAY ONE – ZERO POINT**: Write down everything you're thinking and feeling, both physically and mentally.

_____

_____

_____

_____

_____

_____

→ **DAY ONE – HOUR ONE:** What does it feel like to have followed your rule for one hour? You may not feel any different physically, so concentrate on the mental benefits of confidence, relief from binge anxiety, etc.

_____

_____

_____

_____

_____

_____

_____

_____

_____

_____

_____

_____

_____

_____

_____

➜ **DAY ONE – EIGHT HOUR MARK:** What does it feel like to have followed your rule for eight hours? Depending upon what your rules are, you may begin to feel less bloated and just a little more optimistic. Anything else? Take some notes below.

_____

_____

_____

_____

_____

_____

_____

_____

_____

_____

_____

➜ **DAY TWO – MORNING:** You've been on your Food Plan for approximately one day. What do you observe? Physically? Mentally? Other? What does it feel like to be you, having been on-plan for approximately one full day? Compare this to your Day One Zero Point from yesterday

_____

_____

_____

_____

_____

_____

_____

_____

_____

_____

_____

_____

➔ **DAY TWO – EVENING:** You've been on your Food Plan for approximately two days. What do you observe? Physically? Mentally? Other? What does it feel like to be you, having been on-plan for approximately one full day?

_____

_____

_____

_____

_____

_____

_____

_____

_____

_____

_____

➔ **DAY THREE – MORNING:** What do you observe? Physically? Mentally? Other? What does it feel like to be you, having been on-plan to this point? Compare this to your Day One Zero Point! Compare it to *yesterday* too! What specifically is different and/or new?

_____

_____

_____

_____

_____

_____

_____

_____

_____

_____

_____

_____

_____

➔ **DAY THREE – EVENING:** What do you observe? Physically? Mentally? Other? What does it feel like to be you, having been on-plan for approximately three full days? Compare this to your Day One Zero Point! Compare it to *yesterday* too! What specifically is different and/or new?

_____

_____

_____

_____

_____

_____

_____

_____

_____

_____

_____

_____

_____

_____

_____

→ **DAY FOUR – MORNING:** What do you observe? Physically? Mentally? Other? What does it feel like to be you, having been on-plan to this point? Compare this to your Day One Zero Point! Compare it to *yesterday* too! What specifically is different and/or new?

_____

_____

_____

_____

_____

_____

_____

_____

_____

_____

_____

_____

_____

→ **DAY FOUR – EVENING:** What do you observe? Physically? Mentally? Other? What does it feel like to be you, having been on-plan for approximately four full days? Compare this to your Day One Zero Point! Compare it to *yesterday* too! What specifically is different and/or new?

_____

_____

_____

_____

_____

_____

_____

_____

_____

_____

_____

_____

→ **DAY FIVE – MORNING:** What do you observe? Physically? Mentally? Other? What does it feel like to be you, having been on-plan to this point? Compare this to your Day One Zero Point! Compare it to *yesterday* too! What specifically is different and/or new?

_____

_____

_____

_____

_____

_____

_____

_____

_____

_____

_____

_____

_____

➜ **DAY FIVE – EVENING:** What do you observe? Physically? Mentally? Other? What does it feel like to be you, having been on-plan for approximately five full days? Compare this to your Day One Zero Point! Compare it to *yesterday* too! What specifically is different and/ or new?

_____

_____

_____

_____

_____

_____

_____

_____

_____

_____

_____

➜ **DAY SIX – MORNING:** What do you observe? Physically? Mentally? Other? What does it feel like to be you, having been on-plan to this point? Compare this to your Day One Zero Point! Compare it to *yesterday* too! What specifically is different and/or new?

_____

_____

_____

_____

_____

_____

_____

_____

_____

_____

_____

_____

➜ **DAY SIX – EVENING:** What do you observe? Physically? Mentally? Other? What does it feel like to be you, having been on-plan for approximately six full days? Compare this to your Day One Zero Point! Compare it to *yesterday* too! What specifically is different and/or new?

_____

_____

_____

_____

_____

_____

_____

_____

_____

_____

_____

_____

_____

➜ **DAY SEVEN – MORNING:** What do you observe? Physically? Mentally? Other? What does it feel like to be you, having been on-plan to this point? Compare this to your Day One Zero Point! Compare it to *yesterday* too! What specifically is different and/or new?

_____

_____

_____

_____

_____

_____

_____

_____

_____

_____

_____

→ **DAY SEVEN – EVENING:** What do you observe? Physically? Mentally? Other? What does it feel like to be you, having been on-plan for approximately seven full day? Compare this to your Day One Zero Point! Compare it to *yesterday* too! What specifically is different and/or new?

_____

_____

_____

_____

_____

_____

_____

_____

_____

_____

_____

_____

_____

→ **DAY EIGHT – MORNING:** What do you observe? Physically? Mentally? Other? What does it feel like to be you, having been on-plan to this point? Compare this to your Day One Zero Point! Compare it to *yesterday* too! What specifically is different and/or new?

_____

_____

_____

_____

_____

_____

_____

_____

_____

_____

_____

_____

_____

_____

➔ **DAY EIGHT – EVENING:** What do you observe? Physically? Mentally? Other? What does it feel like to be you, having been on-plan for approximately eight full days? Compare this to your Day One Zero Point! Compare it to *yesterday* too! What specifically is different and/or new?

_____

_____

_____

_____

_____

_____

_____

_____

_____

_____

_____

→ **DAY NINE – MORNING:** What do you observe? Physically? Mentally? Other? What does it feel like to be you, having been on-plan to this point? Compare this to your Day One Zero Point! Compare it to *yesterday* too! What specifically is different and/or new?

\
\
\
\
\
\
\
\
\
\
\
\
\
\

→ **DAY NINE – EVENING:** What do you observe? Physically? Mentally? Other? What does it feel like to be you, having been on-plan for approximately nine full days? Compare this to your Day One Zero Point! Compare it to *yesterday* too! What specifically is different and/or new?

\
\
\
\
\

_____

_____

_____

_____

_____

_____

_____

_____

_____

➔ **DAY TEN – MORNING:** What do you observe? Physically? Mentally? Other? What does it feel like to be you, having been on-plan to this point? Compare this to your Day One Zero Point! Compare it to *yesterday* too! What specifically is different and/or new?

_____

_____

_____

_____

_____

_____

_____

_____

_____

_____

_____

→ **DAY TEN – EVENING:** What do you observe? Physically? Mentally? Other? What does it feel like to be you, having been on-plan for 10 full days!!? Compare this to your Day One Zero Point! Compare it to *yesterday* too! What specifically is different and/or new? **How does it feel to have made it a full ten days?**

_____

_____

_____

_____

_____

_____

_____

_____

_____

_____

_____

_____

Chapter 8

How To Get Back On The Wagon If You Fall Off

(NOTE: THIS SECTION IS NOT FOR YOUR PIG'S EYES)

What do you do if you break your rule? How do you get "back on the wagon" so to speak?

Chapter three of the main book *(Never Binge Again)* "What If You Do Binge?" covers this in detail so I will only summarize the philosophy here, and then leave you with a few exercises. Here are the basics:

→ **If you fall down, get up.** It's the only logical thing to do! Research suggests that people who lose weight permanently differ from those who yo-yo diet indefinitely mostly in their number of attempts. Every failure is one step close to success. "Fall down 7 times, get up 8" – Japanese Proverb

→ **There are two contradictory mindsets which exist in everyone regarding food:** The first is "progress not perfection" and the second is "if you're not perfect then you're nothing."

» **The Pig wants to use "progress not perfection" as a commitment tool.** When you're setting out to follow a rule your Pig would like you to say "just do the best you can, progress not perfection, no need to commit 100%" because it knows that means you'll just try for a little while until you don't feel like it anymore.

» **Likewise, when you make a mistake the Pig will switch to "If you're not perfect, then you're nothing...*so you might as well Binge some more!*"** See how this works? It will try to run excessive guilt around and around in your head until you feel too weak to resist the next overeating episode.

» **The fix for all this is NOT to give up these attitudes, but to completely FLIP when you use them: Commit with perfection but forgive yourself with dignity!** When you're setting out to achieve a goal nothing less than a 100% commitment to that goal will do. But if you're trying to recover from a mistake, that's when you use "progress not perfection." Just reverse what the Pig wants to do 100%.

→ **There are only three causes of a Binge:** (a) your Pig snuck a Squeal by You which you didn't recognize; (b) there was a loophole in one of your Food Rules which let the Pig barrel through. (c) you consciously and purposefully let your Pig out (a "Conscious Pig Party");

» If the problem was (a) Write down the Squeal, and how the Pig was lying to you—*the flaw in its logic*—so you'll recognize it more easily in the future; (b) Tighten up your Food Rule; (c) Go through your day and see if you may have put yourself in a feast and famine state by not eating enough prior to the binge—if that's the case, create a rule which will ensure you do from now on. After this, go through and reconstruct the binge step by step in exquisite detail from the moment you had the first thought that you might binge, through the moment you took the first bite, sip, or swallow, and finally to the point that you decided it was over. Every point along the way was a lever you could've pulled to stop the binge. You can do this next time. Can you see yourself putting the Pig back in the Cage?

» Go through and review your answers to the Big Why Not questions from exercise 2E.

» Go through and re-read your Big Why out loud. *(You've been programming this on a daily basis, right?)*

NOTE: THERE ARE 8 COPIES OF EXERCISE 8A IN THIS BOOK SO YOU CAN USE IT REPEATEDLY IF NEED BE. "FALL DOWN 7 TIMES, GET UP 8!" *(Don't let your Pig know this please)*

➜ **Exercise 8Ai) What caused you to break your rule(s)?**

» **A Squeal I didn't quite recognize**

- Write the Squeal here _____

- Why is this a Squeal, where is the lie in what your Pig said above?

- How will you recognize this Squeal in the future?

» **A loophole in one of my Food Rules**

- What, specifically was the loophole?

- Re-write your rule below to tighten it up please

» **A "Conscious Pig Party" – I knew it was the Pig but I let it out anyway!**

- Write down what you ate for the day PRIOR to breaking your Food Rule(s)

- What was your physical activity level for the day PRIOR to breaking your Food Rule(s)?

- What else and/or who else did you have to take care of PRIOR to breaking your Food Rule(s)? Work tasks, appointments, people, etc. Don't neglect this answer – it's important

- How many breaks did you have for yourself which did not include the requirement you make decisions, answer questions, and/or take care of other people PRIOR to breaking your Food Rule(s)?

- Write out exactly what happened and what you were thinking at every step along the way from the moment you had the first thought to break your Food Rule(s) to the moment you took the first bite, all the way until you decided to STOP the Binge.

_____

_____

_____

- How might you have prevented the Conscious Pig Party if you had it to do over again? How might you have eaten differently that day? How could you have planned more self-care breaks, even just five minutes at a time? Which levers would've been easiest to pull to stop the action chain which led to the binge from the very moment you first thought it might be a "viable" idea?

_____

_____

_____

_____

_____

_____

_____

_____

_____

_____

_____

_____

_____

_____

_____

_____

_____

_____

_____

_____

_____

_____

_____

_____

_____

_____

_____

- Do you need to add, change, modify, or delete any rule in your Food Plan or is the problem solved? If so, write down the changes below. Make sure you've saved a copy of the old Food Plan just in case you need to revert to it later on.

_____

_____

_____

_____

_____

_____

➔ **Exercise 8Bi) Are you 100% confident you will never Binge Again? (YES/NO) - CIRCLE ONE**

» **YES:** Go on to the next section.

» **NO:** Why? Every reason in your head is likely just your Pig Squealing! Write down the Squeals which are bothering you. Why does your Pig say you can't, shouldn't, or won't follow your rules *(as revised above if applicable)* forever?

_____

_____

_____

   ▪ **Which of these Squeals have you already dealt with?** Turn back to Exercise 3A) and review the Squeals along with their logical disputations

   ▪ **Which of these Squeals are NEW?** Add them to Exercise 3A, then look through the list of Common Pig Squeals until you find an answer. Cross reference this answer as before.

» **Exercise 8Ci) Did you call out your Pig? (YES/NO) - CIRCLE ONE.** Once you noticed the thoughts that suggested you break your food plan, did you say "Hey Pig, why do you want me to eat this?". Did you force the Pig to reply? Did you refute it's claims? If not... resolve to do this next time. This is the basic skill to force the Pig out of hiding and make it stop masquerading as You. Using this technique, you can snap yourself out of the trance and notice when the Pig is trying to get one over you!

➔ And that, my friends, is really all you need to do to recover from a Binge. That and be sure you're taking good care of yourself body, mind, and soul. Also, don't skip breakfast tomorrow, even if you feel like you should. Don't try to make up for the Binge with excess exercise, a green juice fast, etc. Just go back to eating healthfully, normally, regularly, and reliably day in and day out. Your body will recover from the poison in your Pig Slop in just a few days, and along with it your confidence!

➔ **Exercise 8Aii) What caused you to break your rule(s)?**

» **A Squeal I didn't quite recognize**

   ▪ Write the Squeal here _____

- Why is this a Squeal, where is the lie in what your Pig said above?

  _____

  _____

  _____

  _____

- How will you recognize this Squeal in the future?

  _____

  _____

  _____

  _____

» **A loophole in one of my Food Rules**

- What, specifically was the loophole?

  _____

  _____

  _____

- Re-write your rule below to tighten it up please

  _____

  _____

  _____

» **A "Conscious Pig Party" – I knew it was the Pig but I let it out anyway!**

- Write down what you ate for the day PRIOR to breaking your Food Rule(s)

  _____

  _____

  _____

- What was your physical activity level for the day PRIOR to breaking your Food Rule(s)?

  _____

  _____

  _____

- What else and/or who else did you have to take care of PRIOR to breaking your Food Rule(s)? Work tasks, appointments, people, etc. Don't neglect this answer – it's important

  _____

  _____

  _____

- How many breaks did you have for yourself which did not include the requirement you make decisions, answer questions, and/or take care of other people PRIOR to breaking your Food Rule(s)?

  _____

  _____

  _____

- Write out exactly what happened and what you were thinking at every step along the way from the moment you had the first thought to break your Food Rule(s) to the moment you took the first bite, all the way until you decided to STOP the Binge.

  _____

  _____

  _____

- How might you have prevented the Conscious Pig Party if you had it to do over again? How might you have eaten differently that day? How could you have planned more self-care breaks, even just five minutes at a time? Which levers would've been easiest to pull to stop the action chain which led to the binge from the very moment you first thought it might be a "viable" idea?

_____

_____

_____

_____

_____

_____

_____

_____

_____

_____

_____

_____

_____

- Do you need to add, change, modify, or delete any rule in your Food Plan or is the problem solved? If so, write down the changes below. Make sure you've saved a copy of the old Food Plan just in case you need to revert to it later on.

_____

_____

_____

_____

_____

_____

➜ **Exercise 8Bii) Are you 100% confident you will never Binge Again? (YES/NO) - CIRCLE ONE**

» **YES:** Go on to the next section.

» **NO:** Why? Every reason in your head is likely just your Pig Squealing! Write down the Squeals which are bothering you. Why does your Pig say you can't, shouldn't, or won't follow your rules *(as revised above if applicable)* forever?

_____

_____

_____

_____

_____

_____

_____

- **Which of these Squeals have you already dealt with?** Turn back to Exercise 3A) and review the Squeals along with their logical disputations

» **Which of these Squeals are NEW?** Add them to Exercise 3A, then look through the list of Common Pig Squeals until you find an answer. Cross reference this answer as before.

➜ **Exercise 8Cii) Did you call out your Pig? (YES/NO) - CIRCLE ONE. Once** you noticed the thoughts that suggested you break your food plan, did you say "Hey Pig, why do you want me to eat this?". Did you force the Pig to reply? Did you refute it's claims? If not... resolve to do this next time. This is the basic skill to force the Pig out of hiding and make it stop masquerading as You. Using this technique, you can snap yourself out of the trance and notice when the Pig is trying to get one over you!

➜ **Exercise 8Aiii) What caused you to break your rule(s)?**

» **A Squeal I didn't quite recognize**

- Write the Squeal here _____

- Why is this a Squeal, where is the lie in what your Pig said above?

  _____

  _____

  _____

  _____

- How will you recognize this Squeal in the future?

  _____

  _____

  _____

  _____

» **A loophole in one of my Food Rules**

- What, specifically was the loophole?

  _____

  _____

  _____

  _____

- Re-write your rule below to tighten it up please

  _____

  _____

  _____

» **A "Conscious Pig Party" – I knew it was the Pig but I let it out anyway!**

- Write down what you ate for the day PRIOR to breaking your Food Rule(s)

  _____

  _____

  _____

- What was your physical activity level for the day PRIOR to breaking your Food Rule(s)?

- What else and/or who else did you have to take care of PRIOR to breaking your Food Rule(s)? Work tasks, appointments, people, etc. Don't neglect this answer — it's important

- How many breaks did you have for yourself which did not include the requirement you make decisions, answer questions, and/or take care of other people PRIOR to breaking your Food Rule(s)?

- Write out exactly what happened and what you were thinking at every step along the way from the moment you had the first thought to break your Food Rule(s) to the moment you took the first bite, all the way until you decided to STOP the Binge.

- How might you have prevented the Conscious Pig Party if you had it to do over again? How might you have eaten differently that day? How could you have planned more self-care breaks, even just five minutes at a time? Which levers would've been easiest to pull to stop the action chain which led to the binge from the very moment you first thought it might be a "viable" idea?

- Do you need to add, change, modify, or delete any rule in your Food Plan or is the problem solved? If so, write down the changes below. Make sure you've saved a copy of the old Food Plan just in case you need to revert to it later on.

_____

_____

_____

_____

_____

_____

➔ **Exercise 8Biii) Are you 100% confident you will never Binge Again? (YES/NO) - CIRCLE ONE**

» **YES:** Go on to the next section.

» **NO:** Why? Every reason in your head is likely just your Pig Squealing! Write down the Squeals which are bothering you. Why does your Pig say you can't, shouldn't, or won't follow your rules *(as revised above if applicable)* forever?

_____

_____

_____

_____

_____

- **Which of these Squeals have you already dealt with?** Turn back to Exercise 3A) and review the Squeals along with their logical disputations

- **Which of these Squeals are NEW?** Add them to Exercise 3A, then look through the list of Common Pig Squeals until you find an answer. Cross reference this answer as before.

→ **Exercise 8Ciii) Did you call out your Pig? (YES/NO) - CIRCLE ONE. Once** you noticed the thoughts that suggested you break your food plan, did you say "Hey Pig, why do you want me to eat this?". Did you force the Pig to reply? Did you refute it's claims? If not... resolve to do this next time. This is the basic skill to force the Pig out of hiding and make it stop masquerading as You. Using this technique, you can snap yourself out of the trance and notice when the Pig is trying to get one over you!

→ **Exercise 8Aiv) What caused you to break your rule(s)?**

» **A Squeal I didn't quite recognize**

▪ Write the Squeal here _____

▪ Why is this a Squeal, where is the lie in what your Pig said above?

_____

_____

_____

▪ How will you recognize this Squeal in the future?

_____

_____

_____

» **A loophole in one of my Food Rules**

▪ What, specifically was the loophole?

_____

_____

_____

▪ Re-write your rule below to tighten it up please

_____

_____

_____

» **A "Conscious Pig Party" – I knew it was the Pig but I let it out anyway!**

- Write down what you ate for the day PRIOR to breaking your Food Rule(s)

  _____

  _____

  _____

- What was your physical activity level for the day PRIOR to breaking your Food Rule(s)?

  _____

  _____

  _____

- What else and/or who else did you have to take care of PRIOR to breaking your Food Rule(s)? Work tasks, appointments, people, etc. Don't neglect this answer – it's important

  _____

  _____

  _____

- How many breaks did you have for yourself which did not include the requirement you make decisions, answer questions, and/or take care of other people PRIOR to breaking your Food Rule(s)?

  _____

  _____

  _____

- Write out exactly what happened and what you were thinking at every step along the way from the moment you had the first thought to break your Food Rule(s) to the moment you took the first bite, all the way until you decided to STOP the Binge.

  _____

  _____

- How might you have prevented the Conscious Pig Party if you had it to do over again? How might you have eaten differently that day? How could you have planned more self-care breaks, even just five minutes at a time? Which levers would've been easiest to pull to stop the action chain which led to the binge from the very moment you first thought it might be a "viable" idea?

- Do you need to add, change, modify, or delete any rule in your Food Plan or is the problem solved? If so, write down the changes below. Make sure you've saved a copy of the old Food Plan just in case you need to revert to it later on.

_____

_____

_____

➔ **Exercise 8Biv) Are you 100% confident you will never Binge Again? (YES/NO) - CIRCLE ONE**

» **YES:** Go on to the next section.

» **NO:** Why? Every reason in your head is likely just your Pig Squealing! Write down the Squeals which are bothering you. Why does your Pig say you can't, shouldn't, or won't follow your rules *(as revised above if applicable)* forever?

_____

_____

_____

_____

_____

- **Which of these Squeals have you already dealt with?** Turn back to Exercise 3A) and review the Squeals along with their logical disputations

- **Which of these Squeals are NEW?** Add them to Exercise 3A, then look through the list of Common Pig Squeals until you find an answer. Cross reference this answer as before.

➔ **Exercise 8Civ) Did you call out your Pig? (YES/NO) - CIRCLE ONE. Once** you noticed the thoughts that suggested you break your food plan, did you say "Hey Pig, why do you want me to eat this?". Did you force the Pig to reply? Did you refute it's claims? If not... resolve to do this next time. This is the basic skill to force the Pig out of hiding and make it stop masquerading as You. Using this technique, you can snap yourself out of the trance and notice when the Pig is trying to get one over you!

→ **Exercise 8Av) What caused you to break your rule(s)?**

» **A Squeal I didn't quite recognize**

- Write the Squeal here _____

- Why is this a Squeal, where is the lie in what your Pig said above?

  _____

  _____

  _____

- How will you recognize this Squeal in the future?

  _____

  _____

  _____

» **A loophole in one of my Food Rules**

- What, specifically was the loophole?

  _____

  _____

  _____

- Re-write your rule below to tighten it up please

  _____

  _____

  _____

» **A "Conscious Pig Party" – I knew it was the Pig but I let it out anyway!**

- Write down what you ate for the day PRIOR to breaking your Food Rule(s)

  _____

  _____

  _____

- What was your physical activity level for the day PRIOR to breaking your Food Rule(s)?

_____

_____

_____

- What else and/or who else did you have to take care of PRIOR to breaking your Food Rule(s)? Work tasks, appointments, people, etc. Don't neglect this answer — it's important

_____

_____

_____

- How many breaks did you have for yourself which did not include the requirement you make decisions, answer questions, and/or take care of other people PRIOR to breaking your Food Rule(s)?

_____

_____

_____

- Write out exactly what happened and what you were thinking at every step along the way from the moment you had the first thought to break your Food Rule(s) to the moment you took the first bite, all the way until you decided to STOP the Binge.

_____

_____

_____

- How might you have prevented the Conscious Pig Party if you had it to do over again? How might you have eaten differently that day? How could you have planned more self-care breaks, even just five minutes at a time? Which levers would've been easiest to pull to stop the action chain which led to the binge from the very moment you first thought it might be a "viable" idea?

- Do you need to add, change, modify, or delete any rule in your Food Plan or is the problem solved? If so, write down the changes below. Make sure you've saved a copy of the old Food Plan just in case you need to revert to it later on.

_____

_____

_____

_____

_____

_____

→ **Exercise 8Bv) Are you 100% confident you will never Binge Again? (YES/NO) - CIRCLE ONE**

» **YES:** Go on to the next section.

» **NO:** Why? Every reason in your head is likely just your Pig Squealing! Write down the Squeals which are bothering you. Why does your Pig say you can't, shouldn't, or won't follow your rules *(as revised above if applicable)* forever?

_____

_____

_____

_____

_____

- **Which of these Squeals have you already dealt with?** Turn back to Exercise 3A) and review the Squeals along with their logical disputations

- **Which of these Squeals are NEW?** Add them to Exercise 3A, then look through the list of Common Pig Squeals until you find an answer. Cross reference this answer as before.

➔ **Exercise 8Cv) Did you call out your Pig? (YES/NO) - CIRCLE ONE. Once** you noticed the thoughts that suggested you break your food plan, did you say "Hey Pig, why do you want me to eat this?". Did you force the Pig to reply? Did you refute it's claims? If not… resolve to do this next time. This is the basic skill to force the Pig out of hiding and make it stop masquerading as You. Using this technique, you can snap yourself out of the trance and notice when the Pig is trying to get one over you!

➔ **Exercise 8Avi) What caused you to break your rule(s)?**

» **A Squeal I didn't quite recognize**

▪ Write the Squeal here _____

▪ Why is this a Squeal, where is the lie in what your Pig said above?

_____

_____

_____

▪ How will you recognize this Squeal in the future?

_____

_____

_____

» **A loophole in one of my Food Rules**

▪ What, specifically was the loophole?

_____

_____

_____

▪ Re-write your rule below to tighten it up please

_____

_____

_____

» **A "Conscious Pig Party" – I knew it was the Pig but I let it out anyway!**

- Write down what you ate for the day PRIOR to breaking your Food Rule(s)

  _____

  _____

  _____

- What was your physical activity level for the day PRIOR to breaking your Food Rule(s)?

  _____

  _____

  _____

- What else and/or who else did you have to take care of PRIOR to breaking your Food Rule(s)? Work tasks, appointments, people, etc. Don't neglect this answer – it's important

  _____

  _____

  _____

- How many breaks did you have for yourself which did not include the requirement you make decisions, answer questions, and/or take care of other people PRIOR to breaking your Food Rule(s)?

  _____

  _____

  _____

- Write out exactly what happened and what you were thinking at every step along the way from the moment you had the first thought to break your Food Rule(s) to the moment you took the first bite, all the way until you decided to STOP the Binge.

  _____

  _____

- How might you have prevented the Conscious Pig Party if you had it to do over again? How might you have eaten differently that day? How could you have planned more self-care breaks, even just five minutes at a time? Which levers would've been easiest to pull to stop the action chain which led to the binge from the very moment you first thought it might be a "viable" idea?

_____

_____

_____

_____

_____

_____

_____

_____

_____

_____

_____

_____

_____

_____

_____

_____

_____

_____

- Do you need to add, change, modify, or delete any rule in your Food Plan or is the problem solved? If so, write down the changes below. Make sure you've saved a copy of the old Food Plan just in case you need to revert to it later on.

_____

_____

_____

_____

_____

_____

→ **Exercise 8Bvi) Are you 100% confident you will never Binge Again? (YES/NO) - CIRCLE ONE**

» **YES:** Go on to the next section.

» **NO:** Why? Every reason in your head is likely just your Pig Squealing! Write down the Squeals which are bothering you. Why does your Pig say you can't, shouldn't, or won't follow your rules *(as revised above if applicable)* forever?

_____

_____

_____

_____

_____

- **Which of these Squeals have you already dealt with?** Turn back to Exercise 3A) and review the Squeals along with their logical disputations

- **Which of these Squeals are NEW?** Add them to Exercise 3A, then look through the list of Common Pig Squeals until you find an answer. Cross reference this answer as before.

→ **Exercise 8Avii) What caused you to break your rule(s)?**

　》 **A Squeal I didn't quite recognize**

　　▪ Write the Squeal here _____

　　▪ Why is this a Squeal, where is the lie in what your Pig said above?

　　_____
　　_____
　　_____

　　▪ How will you recognize this Squeal in the future?

　　_____
　　_____
　　_____

　》 **A loophole in one of my Food Rules**

　　▪ What, specifically was the loophole?

　　_____
　　_____
　　_____

　　▪ Re-write your rule below to tighten it up please

　　_____
　　_____
　　_____

　》 **A "Conscious Pig Party" – I knew it was the Pig but I let it out anyway!**

　　▪ Write down what you ate for the day PRIOR to breaking your Food Rule(s)

　　_____
　　_____
　　_____

- What was your physical activity level for the day PRIOR to breaking your Food Rule(s)?

_____

_____

_____

- What else and/or who else did you have to take care of PRIOR to breaking your Food Rule(s)? Work tasks, appointments, people, etc. Don't neglect this answer — it's important

_____

_____

_____

- How many breaks did you have for yourself which did not include the requirement you make decisions, answer questions, and/or take care of other people PRIOR to breaking your Food Rule(s)?

_____

_____

_____

- Write out exactly what happened and what you were thinking at every step along the way from the moment you had the first thought to break your Food Rule(s) to the moment you took the first bite, all the way until you decided to STOP the Binge.

_____

_____

_____

- How might you have prevented the Conscious Pig Party if you had it to do over again? How might you have eaten differently that day? How could you have planned more self-care breaks, even just five minutes at a time? Which levers would've been easiest to pull to stop the action chain which led to the binge from the very moment you first thought it might be a "viable" idea?

_____

_____

_____

_____

_____

_____

_____

_____

_____

_____

_____

_____

_____

_____

_____

_____

_____

_____

- Do you need to add, change, modify, or delete any rule in your Food Plan or is the problem solved? If so, write down the changes below. Make sure you've saved a copy of the old Food Plan just in case you need to revert to it later on.

_____

_____

_____

_____

_____

_____

➔ **Exercise 8Bvii) Are you 100% confident you will never Binge Again? (YES/NO) - CIRCLE ONE**

» **YES:** Go on to the next section.

» **NO:** Why? Every reason in your head is likely just your Pig Squealing! Write down the Squeals which are bothering you. Why does your Pig say you can't, shouldn't, or won't follow your rules *(as revised above if applicable)* forever?

_____

_____

_____

_____

_____

- **Which of these Squeals have you already dealt with?** Turn back to Exercise 3A) and review the Squeals along with their logical disputations

- **Which of these Squeals are NEW?** Add them to Exercise 3A, then look through the list of Common Pig Squeals until you find an answer. Cross reference this answer as before.

➔ **Exercise 8Aviii) What caused you to break your rule(s)?**

» **A Squeal I didn't quite recognize**

- Write the Squeal here _____

- Why is this a Squeal, where is the lie in what your Pig said above?

  _____

  _____

  _____

- How will you recognize this Squeal in the future?

  _____

  _____

  _____

» **A loophole in one of my Food Rules**

- What, specifically was the loophole?

  _____

  _____

  _____

- Re-write your rule below to tighten it up please

  _____

  _____

  _____

» **A "Conscious Pig Party" – I knew it was the Pig but I let it out anyway!**

- Write down what you ate for the day PRIOR to breaking your Food Rule(s)

  _____

  _____

  _____

- What was your physical activity level for the day PRIOR to breaking your Food Rule(s)?

_____

_____

_____

- What else and/or who else did you have to take care of PRIOR to breaking your Food Rule(s)? Work tasks, appointments, people, etc. Don't neglect this answer – it's important

_____

_____

_____

- How many breaks did you have for yourself which did not include the requirement you make decisions, answer questions, and/or take care of other people PRIOR to breaking your Food Rule(s)?

_____

_____

_____

- Write out exactly what happened and what you were thinking at every step along the way from the moment you had the first thought to break your Food Rule(s) to the moment you took the first bite, all the way until you decided to STOP the Binge.

_____

_____

_____

- How might you have prevented the Conscious Pig Party if you had it to do over again? How might you have eaten differently that day? How could you have planned more self-care breaks, even just five minutes at a time? Which levers would've been easiest to pull to stop the action chain which led to the binge from the very moment you first thought it might be a "viable" idea?

- Do you need to add, change, modify, or delete any rule in your Food Plan or is the problem solved? If so, write down the changes below. Make sure you've saved a copy of the old Food Plan just in case you need to revert to it later on.

➡ **Exercise 8Bviii) Are you 100% confident you will never Binge Again? (YES/NO) - CIRCLE ONE**

» **YES:** Go on to the next section.

» **NO:** Why? Every reason in your head is likely just your Pig Squealing! Write down the Squeals which are bothering you. Why does your Pig say you can't, shouldn't, or won't follow your rules *(as revised above if applicable)* forever?

- **Which of these Squeals have you already dealt with?** Turn back to Exercise 3A) and review the Squeals along with their logical disputations

- **Which of these Squeals are NEW?** Add them to Exercise 3A, then look through the list of Common Pig Squeals until you find an answer. Cross reference this answer as before.

➔ **Exercise 8Cviii) Did you call out your Pig? (YES/NO) - CIRCLE ONE. Once** you noticed the thoughts that suggested you break your food plan, did you say "Hey Pig, why do you want me to eat this?". Did you force the Pig to reply? Did you refute it's claims? If not... resolve to do this next time. This is the basic skill to force the Pig out of hiding and make it stop masquerading as You. Using this technique, you can snap yourself out of the trance and notice when the Pig is trying to get one over you!

Chapter 9

When And How To Add More Rules

I hope it's dawned on you that what we're trying to do here is a LOT more than just lose weight. What we're doing with Never Binge Again is giving you the tools to escape the diet mentality and *become a different kind of person with food* than you've ever been before. Character trumps willpower. In the end, finding lasting peace with food is all about escaping the diet mentality and changing how you relate to food.

Towards this end, I want you to focus more on your general wellbeing, and on your ability to move difficult food decisions from your emotions and impulses to your intellect by staying on your Food Plan. Once these two tremendous abilities are firmly entrenched, you can begin to measure your results in some way which is meaningful to you—*the scale, how your clothing fits, etc.* Then you gradually adjust your Food Plan to achieve weight loss and/or other health and fitness goals.

On the other hand, if you allow weight loss to become your priority, you'll want to make rules to do it too quickly. This then activates your feast and famine drive and makes it MUCH harder to manage cravings.

"Direction is more important than speed." – Doug Graham, author of "The 80-10-10 Diet."

"The fastest way to lose weight is slowly." – ME – I said that! It's true because otherwise you stimulate the drive to put it all back on, and more.

Our culture's constant focus on weight loss and thinness is the cause of relentless misery. It's why so many people have the experience of being able to be good for a little while...until every bone in their body screams "eat it" and they find it next to impossible to continue following their rules.

The "diet mentality" fuels the Pig. Let's not do that anymore, OK?

Why am I saying this NOW? Because once we've restored your confidence in your ability to control your eating by following your One Simple Rule for a while, you're going to be very tempted to add a multitude of very restrictive rules in an attempt to lose weight quickly. But if you focus more on your newfound sense of wellbeing, health, and confidence, it turns out to be a lot easier to gradually adjust your diet to get where you need to go!

In this section we are going to focus on a procedure for adding more rules to gradually accomplish weight loss and other goals. It's a lot less complicated than you may think.

PLEASE DO NOT PROCEED WITH THIS SECTION UNTIL YOU HAVE REMAINED ON ANY FOOD PLAN (INCLUDING ONE SIMPLE RULE) FOR AT LEAST 10 DAYS.

Exercise 9A) Write down what you specifically want to achieve by adjusting your Food Plan:

➔ _____

_____

_____

_____

_____

_____

_____

_____

Exercise 9B) Adding Rules for Weight Loss. If you do not wish to lose weight, skip this exercise. If your goal IS generally related to weight loss, you will most likely need to add at least one rule which regulates portions, volume, or the type of food you eat. Sometimes it's also possible to lose weight by changing food behaviors—for example, by only ever eating again when you're sitting at a table with a knife and fork, etc.

➔ **9Bi) Weight Loss Desired:** How much weight do you want to lose? _____

➔ **9Bii) Weekly Weight Loss Rate:** What might be a realistic weekly rate at which you could lose it? *(No more than 2 pounds per week unless your doctor overrides this. Most people are more successful with just one pound per week, or even a half pound per week)* _____

➔ **9Biii) Weeks to Goal:** Divide 8Bi by 8Bii. This is the number of weeks it will take you to lose the weight at the rate above. _____

➔ **9Biv) Projected Date of Goal Achievement:** Add the number of weeks calculated in 8Biii to today's date. This is approximately when you will achieve your goal if you lose weight at the rate in 8Bii. Write down this projected date _____

  » **Projected Quarter Way Point (QWP):** Multiply 8Biii by 0.25, then add the resulting number of weeks to today's date. This is your Quarter Way Point. Write down the projected date _____, and what you will weigh at that time _____.

  » **Projected Halfway Point (HWP):** Multiply 8Biii by 0.50, then add the resulting number of weeks to today's date. This is your Halfway Point. Write down the projected date _____, and what you will weigh at that time _____.

» **Projected Three Quarter Way Point (3QWP):** Multiply 8Biii by 0.75, then add the resulting number of weeks to today's date. This is your Three Quarter Way Point. Write down the projected date _____, and what you will weigh at that time _____.

» **Take a breath.** Then imagine yourself at the weights at each point above. How will that feel? I'm trying to ground you in the notion that the journey will feel progressively more rewarding all along the way, not just when you achieve your ideal weight.

➔ **9Bv) Weekly Deficit Required:** Multiply your answer to 8Bii above by 3500 _____. (It takes a 3500 calorie surplus over your month's requirements to gain one pound, and 3500 under to lose one. If you aren't clear how calorie surpluses and deficits are related to weight loss and/or weight gain, you can watch a video on www.WorkbookExamples.com

➔ **9Bvi) Daily Deficit Required (DDR):** Divide your answer to 8Biii above by 7. This is the daily deficit we will need to create. _____

➔ **9Bvii) Assessing the Daily Deficit: How realistic is it to achieve?**

» **What food and/or treats might be moderated and/or eliminated to achieve the DDR:** Using a tracking site like Cronometer.com or MyFitnessPal.com, enter a typical day of food and assess your daily intake. Usually the easiest way to begin losing weight is to cut some calories from empty and/or low-nutrient-density foods. This way you are cutting calories without cutting too much nutrition, and cravings can be kept at a lower level. What "empty" and/or low-nutrient density foods might you cut down on each day *(or every other day, etc.)* in order to create the DDR? Please note that most people have an intuitive sense of where they are getting their extra calories. Take a breath. Where are your extra calories coming from?

_____

_____

_____

_____

_____

_____

» **What activities might you add to your daily and/or weekly routines in order to help achieve the DDR, and to prevent you from having to eliminate too much food?** How often would you need to do them?

» **How might you adjust your Food Rule(s) to achieve the above?** Note: By this point you'll want to be keeping a full Food Plan on either a separate piece of paper or via the template provided on the next page. You can download a copy of this template by signing up for the free reader bonuses via the Big Red Button on www.NeverBingeAgain.com. Go ahead and adjust your plan now.

YOU WILL FIND EIGHT FOOD PLAN TEMPLATES IN THE NEXT 8 PAGES FOR YOUR CONVENIENCE!

(If you are at all confused about how and when you may change your Food Plan please read the "How to Change Your Food Plan" section of Never Binge Again.)

DISCLAIMER: If you don't already know how to cut out foods from your diet while maintaining a fully nutritious diet then you must consult a licensed dietician. No nutritional advice is offered in this and/or any of our books as we do not have the credentials and/or experience to tell you what to eat. However, we have observed many clients try to lose weight too quickly with nutritionally and/or calorically inadequate Food Plans. This keeps them stuck in the feast-and-famine cycle and makes their eating problems worse, not better. Therefore, we take this opportunity to remind you how necessary it is for you to create a nutritionally complete Food Plan which does NOT restrict calories too severely. Otherwise, the rest of your precious work and efforts will be for naught. (When nutrition and/or calories are too scarce the brain wants to force you to be less discriminating about food and your rules will go out the window!)

FOOD PLAN TEMPLATE #1

Enter Date Here _____

Please note you can use this template to create rules
that address the goal to lose, gain, and/or maintain weight!

NEVERS	ALWAYS	UNRESTRICTED	CONDITIONALS
What foods, drinks, and behaviors will you never indulge in again as long as you live?	What will you always do regarding food, drink, and food behaviors?	What foods, drinks, and food behaviors will you permit yourself to have without restriction?	What foods, drinks, and behaviors will you permit only at certain times, in certain amounts, and/or restricted by other conditions?

FOOD PLAN TEMPLATE #2

Enter Date Here _____

Please note you can use this template to create rules
that address the goal to lose, gain, and/or maintain weight!

NEVERS	ALWAYS	UNRESTRICTED	CONDITIONALS
What foods, drinks, and behaviors will you never indulge in again as long as you live?	What will you always do regarding food, drink, and food behaviors?	What foods, drinks, and food behaviors will you permit yourself to have without restriction?	What foods, drinks, and behaviors will you permit only at certain times, in certain amounts, and/ or restricted by other conditions?

FOOD PLAN TEMPLATE #3

Enter Date Here _____

*Please note you can use this template to create rules
that address the goal to lose, gain, and/or maintain weight!*

NEVERS	ALWAYS	UNRESTRICTED	CONDITIONALS
What foods, drinks, and behaviors will you never indulge in again as long as you live?	What will you always do regarding food, drink, and food behaviors?	What foods, drinks, and food behaviors will you permit yourself to have without restriction?	What foods, drinks, and behaviors will you permit only at certain times, in certain amounts, and/ or restricted by other conditions?

FOOD PLAN TEMPLATE #4

Enter Date Here _____

*Please note you can use this template to create rules
that address the goal to lose, gain, and/or maintain weight!*

NEVERS	ALWAYS	UNRESTRICTED	CONDITIONALS
What foods, drinks, and behaviors will you never indulge in again as long as you live?	What will you always do regarding food, drink, and food behaviors?	What foods, drinks, and food behaviors will you permit yourself to have without restriction?	What foods, drinks, and behaviors will you permit only at certain times, in certain amounts, and/or restricted by other conditions?

FOOD PLAN TEMPLATE #5

Enter Date Here _____

*Please note you can use this template to create rules
that address the goal to lose, gain, and/or maintain weight!*

NEVERS	ALWAYS	UNRESTRICTED	CONDITIONALS
What foods, drinks, and behaviors will you never indulge in again as long as you live?	What will you always do regarding food, drink, and food behaviors?	What foods, drinks, and food behaviors will you permit yourself to have without restriction?	What foods, drinks, and behaviors will you permit only at certain times, in certain amounts, and/or restricted by other conditions?

FOOD PLAN TEMPLATE #6

Enter Date Here _____

*Please note you can use this template to create rules
that address the goal to lose, gain, and/or maintain weight!*

NEVERS	ALWAYS	UNRESTRICTED	CONDITIONALS
What foods, drinks, and behaviors will you never indulge in again as long as you live?	What will you always do regarding food, drink, and food behaviors?	What foods, drinks, and food behaviors will you permit yourself to have without restriction?	What foods, drinks, and behaviors will you permit only at certain times, in certain amounts, and/ or restricted by other conditions?

FOOD PLAN TEMPLATE #7

Enter Date Here _____

Please note you can use this template to create rules
that address the goal to lose, gain, and/or maintain weight!

NEVERS	ALWAYS	UNRESTRICTED	CONDITIONALS
What foods, drinks, and behaviors will you never indulge in again as long as you live?	What will you always do regarding food, drink, and food behaviors?	What foods, drinks, and food behaviors will you permit yourself to have without restriction?	What foods, drinks, and behaviors will you permit only at certain times, in certain amounts, and/or restricted by other conditions?

FOOD PLAN TEMPLATE #8

Enter Date Here _____

*Please note you can use this template to create rules
that address the goal to lose, gain, and/or maintain weight!*

NEVERS	ALWAYS	UNRESTRICTED	CONDITIONALS
What foods, drinks, and behaviors will you never indulge in again as long as you live?	What will you always do regarding food, drink, and food behaviors?	What foods, drinks, and food behaviors will you permit yourself to have without restriction?	What foods, drinks, and behaviors will you permit only at certain times, in certain amounts, and/ or restricted by other conditions?

Special Rule Circumstances:

➔ **If you are having trouble deciding between a "Never" vs. a "Conditional":** If you can't decide, then write out the rule both ways first. Then do Exercise 2B starting with each rule. In other words, project yourself one year in the future under the presumption you adopted one rule, then the other. Compare and contrast and you should have your answer.

➔ **Accumulating Too Many Rules:** Sometimes clients come to me with literally dozens of rules. Generally speaking, the majority of these rules are an attempt to moderate a particular food category. For example, I remember one client who had 32 rules regarding when she was allowed to have sugar. I said to her *"why don't we just say 'the only sweet tastes I'll ever consume again are X, Y, and Z except (short list of conditions)."*

Sometimes that works to simplify and solve the issue. Other times it turns out the long list of Food Rules around a particular category of food is really an attempt to come to terms with the fact that a "never" rule is in order. For example, "I will never eat sugar again" vs. 32 ways sugar might be OK. But only the person who owns the rule knows whether this is the case for sure.

Fewer rules are better. Simpler rules are better. But no fewer and/or simpler than is necessary to cover all your dangerous trigger foods and behaviors so that you can protect your health and fitness goals. Most successful Food Plans I've seen have had 7 or less rules. My personal Food Plan at the moment has only four. I've had clients who've achieved all their goals with only ONE rule. Others who required 15 or more. It really depends on your situation, needs, and motivation. This may change over time as your life, experience, and wisdom evolves.

➔ **Serious Eating Disorders**: Legally I don't make any claims regarding Never Binge Again's ability to help with ANY diagnosed eating disorder even though there are hundreds of people who say that it has. I was perhaps diagnosable as an exercise bulimic at one point in my life. Never Binge Again is the solution I developed for my unique personal struggles. I never purged *(I tried one time – it didn't suit me)*, nor did I ever develop a fear of food and/or any type of habitual undereating and/or problem with being underweight.

Furthermore, although at this point I've worked with hundreds of overeaters, I do so as a coach, not a licensed psychologist, and therefore don't go through a rigorous diagnosis and treatment process. Prior to developing Never Binge Again for myself I referred the vast majority of eating disordered clients out to other professionals since I felt I had a serious problem myself and wasn't in a position to treat them. I therefore don't have any consistent information and/or data about Never Binge Again's ability to help people with serious eating disorders like bulimia, anorexia, etc.

That said, some clients who have been classified with one of these diagnoses by their doctor have reported some success using the method.

People with Bulimia who have reported success with NBA tell me they have to abide by one rule over and above all else "I will never purge again!" When they allow themselves to purge, it seems all the other Pig's Squeals get louder. Because the essence of all Pig Squeal is that it "doesn't matter" if you Binge one more time, the very real notion that the calories won't count because you can "get rid" of them undermines every other principle in the Never Binge Again system. Most of these people have gained weight during the months following their no purging rule, but they say it was worth it because they feel so much better. Some, but not all of these people lost the weight back.

Far fewer people with Anorexia have reported success to me, but those who have seem to have taken to the notion that their "hunger and full meters are broken." They used their Food Rules and Food Plan as a whole to intellectually define—*usually with the help of a licensed dietitian and/or their doctor*—what healthy eating looks like. They rely on the mantra "feelings aren't facts" when they hear their Pig Squealing for them to break their Food Plan. And they do their best to stick to it.

→ **Needing to gain weight rather than lose it.** Go through the entirety of Exercise 8B doing calculations for a SURPLUS rather than a deficit. You can still project the timeline, etc.

Chapter 10

Dealing With Travel, Restaurants, Social Pressure, Holidays, And Other Piggy Exceptions!

Put your hands over your Pig's eyes please while you read this, but it would be helpful for you to know that in the natural course of a successful progression through Never Binge Again, most people tend to do well for a while at first when they're at home and can more easily control their food inventory, routines, time, and social interaction around food...

But they suddenly fall down when they hit what I call a "Piggy Exception."

A Piggy Exception is any place, situation, and/or time where you find it particularly difficult to stay on your Food Plan, or where Pig Squeals seem especially loud and alluring.

Often people can successfully manage these situations with a concept I call "the second rung of the archery target." If you think of your everyday Food Plan as your bullseye on an archery target, you can also set a clearly defined boundary for the second—and even third—rung of this target, representing specifically how your rules expand when you encounter one of these difficult situations.

For example, perhaps you have a rule which says "I'll never again eat anything sweet except for whole fruit, berries, and stevia." But you find it very difficult to stick to this rule on Holidays. So you make the rule a Conditional instead of a Never. *"Except on Thanksgiving, Christmas, and New Year's Day when I may have one (and only one) serving of the dessert of my choice, I'll never again eat anything sweet except for whole fruit, berries, and stevia!"* Then you may wish to add something to the definitions section of your Food Plan which clearly defines what "one serving" of dessert is.

In this way you have made all the difficult decisions beforehand and eliminated the need to rely upon willpower in the previously tempting situation. You simply shoot for the second rung of the archery target instead of the bullseye. It's a wider, but still very specifically defined target. You'll know with certainty whether you hit it or you missed it.

Many (but not all) people find that shooting for the second rung of a well-defined archery target makes it possible to control themselves in situations which previously felt impossible. There is always a risk involved if you are truly addicted to something however, that you may find it too difficult to have ANY of it. Only you know whether this is a risk worth taking. For example, I personally never risk eating chocolate, but I DO allow other things which aren't on my everyday Food Plan on special occasions, in very specific amounts, and I do just fine.

Decisions wear down your willpower. Making your difficult food decisions before you enter a tempting situation preserves your willpower for more important things and often lets you coast through situations you couldn't resist overeating in before.

Exercise 10A) Prioritize the "Piggy Exceptions" for which you'll need to consider pre-planning and/or adjusting your rules. Using each of the numbers from 1 to 4 *only* one time each, where 1 = "least frequently a dangerous eating environment" and 4 means "most frequently a dangerous eating environment" rank order the following situations:

➔ TRAVEL _____

➔ RESTAURANTS _____

➔ SOCIAL PRESSURE TO OVEREAT _____

➔ HOLIDAYS _____

Exercise 10B) Go through the bulleted sections below, one at a time, beginning with the one from 10A above which you ranked as MOST dangerous, then next most, all the way through to least dangerous. This may take you several days. There's no need to rush.

➔ **10Bi) TRAVEL**

  » **How often do you travel? _____ *(days per year)***

  » **What does your Pig typically get you to binge on when you do?**

  _____

  _____

  _____

  _____

  _____

  _____

  » **How do you feel after you binge when you travel?**

  _____

  _____

  _____

  _____

  _____

  _____

» **How much time and energy does it take you to recover from eating Pig Slop when you travel**? *(Hint — a lot! But make a specific estimate per day). Why?*

» **How does recovering from eating Pig Slop impact the original purpose of your travel?** For example, if you were hoping to have a productive business trip, how much more productive could it have been if you didn't eat the Slop? If you were taking the trip for pleasure with friends or family, etc., how much more might you have enjoyed your time if you'd been free of Slop? Why do you say that?

» **Think of the next trip you're planning.** If you don't have any travel planned right now, answer retrospectively about a *previous* trip.

   ▪ **Will it be remotely possible to stop at a supermarket** before you arrive at your destination? Open a web browser and search for "supermarket XXXXX" where "XXXXX" is the city and zip code of your destination. Write down the address of two supermarkets here:

- *NOTE: If you could not find a supermarket in the city of your destination, search for a supermarket using the same syntax above, but in the nearest major city along the way to your destination.*

- **What could you pick up at the supermarket** to keep with you, either in the hotel, which will usually bring a small refrigerator to your room for a small fee if you ask, or in the rental car if you'll have one and the temperature is suitable. For example, apples, bananas, oranges, tomatoes, etc. are fairly ubiquitous and don't necessarily even require refrigeration.

  _____

  _____

  _____

  _____

  _____

- **What might you carry with you in your purse and/or briefcase?**

  _____

  _____

  _____

  _____

  _____

- **Look at your schedule for your travel time.** Walk through several, if not all of the days.

  - When and where are your eating opportunities?

    _____

    _____

    _____

    _____

    _____

- When and where will you be forced to go through too long a period without the opportunity to eat a healthy meal? List every difficult juncture below:

_____

_____

_____

_____

_____

_____

- How might you solve this without resorting to Pig Slop? *(Hint: Your Pig says it can't be done)*

_____

_____

_____

_____

_____

» **A few notes for your consideration. Place a checkmark next to each one after you've read them please:**

- Eating healthy when you travel is your FIRST priority, because when you don't do it everything else suffers.

- If you have time to look at your email, you have time to plan and eat healthy

- If you have time to do Facebook, you have time to plan and eat healthy

- If you have time to make phone calls, you have time to plan and eat healthy

- Thirty minutes of extra self-care with food should buy you at least 90 minutes of extra productivity compared to eating Pig Slop

» **After considering everything above, how** *(if at all)* **might you like to revise your Food Rules for travel?** Would you like to utilize the "2nd rung of the archery target" concept to create conditionals in any way? Write down the specific rule modification below, copy it to your Food Plan, and implement it in your Food Rules in 24 hours. *(Make sure to keep a backup of your Food Plan whenever you change it.)*

_____

_____

_____

_____

_____

_____

➔ **10Bii) RESTAURANTS: Your Pig thinks restaurants are the PERFECT opportunity to Binge!!** After all, their entire business model rests on feeding it. The lighting, menu, and presentation of the food and dessert tray is designed to stimulate your Pig. Plus, there is the social pressure to eat like everyone else there is eating, and your genuine need to enjoy the food and company! But there are many things you can do to 100% successfully Cage the Pig in a restaurant. Think about an upcoming restaurant meal which may become a trigger situation:

» **Can you eat beforehand and make the meal more about the company than the restaurant food and ENJOY your friends/colleagues/family?** Focus on helping them talk and feel good about themselves?

▪ When and what would you eat before going?

_____

_____

_____

_____

_____

- Who will you be seeing at the restaurant?

  _____

  _____

  _____

  _____

  _____

- What are some interesting questions you could plan to ask these specific people in order to stimulate a meaningful conversation?

  _____

  _____

  _____

  _____

  _____

» **Are there some ingredients you'd feel good about which you can take with you in your purse, etc.?** For example, some people keep nuts, seeds, or even dried chickpeas with them and throw them in the salad at the restaurant for extra non-Slop calories. Write them here:

  _____

  _____

  _____

  _____

  _____

» **Researching the menu:** Pick a restaurant to practice researching and preparing for on-line. If it's one you'll be visiting shortly, great! Otherwise pick one you haven't been to before for practice. Perhaps Google something like "Italian restaurant near ZIPCODE" *(replace with actual zip code)* and pick one that looks interesting.

- Are there any dishes on the menu consistent with your Food Plan? List them here:

_____

_____

_____

_____

_____

_____

- What ingredients WITHIN the dishes are consistent with your Food Plan? You can ask the waiter/chef for a special dish to be created from these ingredients. List them here:

_____

_____

_____

_____

_____

_____

- What might you eat, specifically, if you were to visit this restaurant?

_____

_____

_____

_____

_____

» **After considering everything above, how** *(if at all)* **might you like to revise your Food Rules for restaurants?** Would you like to utilize the "2nd rung of the archery target" concept to create conditionals in any way? Write down the specific rule modification below, copy it to your Food Plan, and implement it in your Food Rules in 24 hours. *(Make sure to keep a backup of your Food Plan whenever you change it.)*

_____

_____

_____

_____

_____

_____

_____

_____

_____

➔ **10Biii) SOCIAL PRESSURE**: There is a lot more than what you see on the surface fueling the social pressure you experience from other people to eat Pig Slop. Sure, people would prefer you ate what they were eating for taste, convenience, and comfort. But did you ever stop to consider that there may have been a time when the survival of the tribe depended on everyone eating the same thing?

First of all, sometimes only one nutrition and calorie source may have been available. Moreover, this food may have been scarce, and all members of the tribe may have been necessary to execute the labor required to survive. If you refused to eat what everyone else was eating you risked becoming weak and sick... not only unable to work, but an extra burden to the tribe.

Then there is the custom of warring tribes "breaking bread" at a meal together to indicate a peace treaty. Eating the same thing as everyone else tells the tribe "we are not here to rape, pillage, and plunder, we come in peace as your ally now."

And the military's need to supply calories and nutrition to soldiers cross vast distances too long to reliably transport fruit, vegetables, and other high nutrition density foods. *(At least before the advent of airplane travel).*

There are other reasons which I'll write about someday, but the bottom line is that the pressure you feel to eat what everyone else is eating when you dine with others is very real, and stems from the desire for cohesive and consistent tribe survival.

The upshot of all this is that it's usually a big mistake to debate what's "healthy" vs. "unhealthy" with people who are pressuring you to eat what they want you to eat. It's simultaneously quite important to understand that it's NEVER necessary to eat anything you've defined as Pig Slop for yourself just to make others feel comfortable...

Because the social pressure from other people can be neutralized by giving them what they really want...and what they REALLY want is to feel loved, safe, and to believe it's OK for them to eat what they want to. *But you don't give them this reassurance directly.* Instead, you use something I call "The Alternative Love Gift" technique.

It's very simple. If Mom offers me a piece of chocolate cake when I walk in the house, I understand her to just be trying to welcome me back into the tribe after not seeing me for a while. Unconsciously she is saying "here, this is how we love you in this tribe, won't you accept?" Since I have personally defined chocolate as Pig Slop, I need to find a way to not eat it without offending her. She IS trying to love me, after all, even if I don't experience it that way.

What I do NOT say is "see Mom, I've found I'm addicted to chocolate because it's got all sorts of stimulants and drugs in it, not to mention all the fat and sugar." What I want to do instead is provide her with an alternative way she can love me and welcome me back into the tribe WITHOUT making an issue of the cake. Gently show her how she can offer you an Alternative Love Gift. Any of the following should work: (1) "Mom, you know what? I'm a little cold. Does Michael (her husband) maybe have a sweater you could let me wear tonight? (2) Mom, you know what? I ate a little too much at lunch and my stomach is a little upset. Do you have any mint tea by any chance? (3) Mom, that's so sweet! But you know what? I'm going CRAZY to know the score of the game tonight. Is there ANY chance we could turn on the TV for just a second?

All of these will make Mom happy because she now has a way to love you back into the tribe AND there's been nothing said which will make her feel rejected and/or guilty about eating the cake herself.

» Brainstorm several "Alternative Love Gift" ideas you could use when you feel pressure to eat Pig Slop from others in a social situation. Write out specifically who you imagine the pressure coming from, and what, specifically you might ask for to solve the problem. Write down as many ideas as you can think of below.

» **After considering everything above, how** *(if at all)* **might you like to revise your Food Rules for social situations?** Would you like to utilize the "2nd rung of the archery target" concept to create conditionals in any way? Write down the specific rule modification below, copy it to your Food Plan, and implement it in your Food Rules in 24 hours. *(Make sure to keep a backup of your Food Plan whenever you change it.)* Be sure to specifically define what constitutes a social situation if you are going to create Conditional rules for them.

_____

_____

_____

_____

_____

_____

_____

_____

_____

_____

➔ **10Biv) HOLIDAYS:** Holidays are really just special instances of social meal gatherings. However, people like to consider them separately because they occur infrequently, and because they feel a lot more pressure than usual to eat what they consider Slop.

» Before you make a Conditional rule for the Holidays you may wish to consider any health risks you are facing. Research suggests the highest spike in mortality from cardiovascular events like heart attacks and strokes, for example, occur right around the Holidays.

» That said, a lot of people find they eat much better utilizing the second rung of the archery target approach on the Holidays than completely abstaining from the treats available. A very common example is "Despite all my other rules, on Thanksgiving, Christmas, and New Year's Day I will permit myself one plate of main-dish food with anything I like, and one serving of any dessert I choose."

» **After considering everything above, how** *(if at all)* **might you like to revise your Food Rules for social situations?** Would you like to utilize the "2nd rung of the archery target" concept to create conditionals in any way? Write down the specific rule modification below, copy it to your Food Plan, and implement it in your Food Rules in 24 hours. *(Make sure to keep a backup of your Food Plan whenever you change it.)*

Chapter 11

Collecting Daily Evidence Of Success

The Reptilian Brain is defeatist. It wants you to think the possibility of gaining control and eating healthy in a more permanent way is *entirely* out of reach. Why? So it can binge more, of course!

Accordingly, the central tactic it deploys is an effort to get you to focus squarely on your failures. *The Reptilian Brain wants you to collect evidence of failure at every turn!* It will pound the gavel, beat you down, and shame you about every last mistake… ignoring any and all progress you may have made because you weren't perfect. When this attitude persists long enough, you develop a "failure identity" and overeating becomes much more frequent and intense…

But you do NOT have to allow this to happen—and you can reverse it if it already has—by collecting evidence of success instead! OK, so you had a binge. But did you stop at 5 cupcakes instead of 15? Brilliant! Write it down. Ate only one whole box of muffins instead of two? Give yourself credit. Stopped at 5,000 extra calories instead of 10,000? You get the idea.

On the other hand, if you had a GOOD eating day, why? Perhaps you had some extra self-care. Maybe you made sure to eat more substantially in a whole and natural way. Perhaps you attended more carefully to the frequency of your meals, so you never let your blood sugar get too low.

There is ALWAYS something you can learn from a day's experience, no matter whether you followed your Food Plan or not!

I've therefore left the following 8 templates for you to write down everything you did RIGHT each day. I want you to use them to establish a daily habit of collecting evidence of success! But don't stop at 8 days, that's just to get you going. I'd like you to do this EVERY day for at least the next few months. This habit—collecting evidence of success—more than any other, makes the biggest difference for our clients!

Doing this first thing in the morning (along with any other journaling) is most effective, but not required.

EXERCISE 11 – INCLUDES EIGHT TEMPLATES COLLECTING EVIDENCE OF SUCCESS DAY ONE

WHAT DID YOU DO RIGHT YESTERDAY?

_____

(Insert Date)

COLLECTING EVIDENCE OF SUCCESS DAY TWO

WHAT DID YOU DO RIGHT YESTERDAY?

_____

(Insert Date)

COLLECTING EVIDENCE OF SUCCESS DAY THREE

WHAT DID YOU DO RIGHT YESTERDAY?

_____

(Insert Date)

COLLECTING EVIDENCE OF SUCCESS DAY FOUR

WHAT DID YOU DO RIGHT YESTERDAY?

————————————

(Insert Date)

COLLECTING EVIDENCE OF SUCCESS DAY FIVE

WHAT DID YOU DO RIGHT YESTERDAY?

_____

(Insert Date)

COLLECTING EVIDENCE OF SUCCESS DAY SIX

WHAT DID YOU DO RIGHT YESTERDAY?

_____

(Insert Date)

COLLECTING EVIDENCE OF SUCCESS DAY SEVEN

WHAT DID YOU DO RIGHT YESTERDAY?

_____

(Insert Date)

COLLECTING EVIDENCE OF SUCCESS DAY EIGHT

WHAT DID YOU DO RIGHT YESTERDAY?

_____

(Insert Date)

Chapter 12

Embracing The Never Binge Again Principles In Full

Try to answer the following questions to the best of your ability. The "lesson to learn" follows each question on its own separate page. Don't read ahead please or you'll ruin it! Also, please note that even if your Pig feels you "already know" the answers to these questions, the act of writing out detailed answers in black and white will more thoroughly stamp it into your way of being in the world. So, don't let your Pig deprive you of this opportunity with the four deadliest words in the world *"We already know this!"*

➜ **Exercise 12 – Never Binge Again Principle Immersion**

　》 **12A) QUESTION: True or False? It's very important to channel as much of your mental energy as possible into hoping you will be able to remain on your Food Plan. If possible one should pray for this ability each day too.** Please support your answer with detailed notes. Why is or isn't this true? Write your answer below.

» **12A) ANSWER: False!** Inherent in both hoping and praying for the ability to stay on your Food Plan is the notion that control must be bestowed upon you by a benevolent power outside yourself if and only if it is pleased with your connection with it. In contrast, neurologically speaking, you have the power to resist any temptation. It's wired right into your brain. Therefore, Never Binge Again asserts we should declare ourselves 110% confident we will Never Binge Again and assume any thoughts, feelings, images, or impulses which suggest otherwise are the Pig. Therefore, hoping and praying for the ability to stick to your Food Rules is a Pig's game. It's the Pig's way of getting you to admit it is more powerful than you!

» **12B) QUESTION: True or False? Emotional upset is the primary cause of overeating and binge eating. It's therefore critical to learn alternative ways to cope with your emotions in order to stay on your Food Plan.** Please support your answer with detailed notes. Why is or isn't this true? Write your answer below.

» **12B ANSWER):** One of the primary principles of Never Binge Again is the subjugation of emotion to intellect where dangerous food decisions are concerned. Prior to Never Binge Again, most people have allowed their Pig to convince them "emotional eating" was the cause of their overeating problem, but it wasn't. See, uncomfortable emotions may trigger the desire to get high with food, but there always must be an intervening voice of justification that rationalizes the indulgence. That voice which makes it "OK" to eat 12 bars of chocolate because you feel lonely, brokenhearted, or depressed. The Pig's voice, perpetually present and looking for ways to convince you it's worth eating some Slop.

But here's the thing almost nobody realizes: The belief emotional upset must be dealt with *before* we can stop overeating causes us to fuel the emotional upset itself. Think about it, if the Pig knows it's going to get fed if it upsets you enough, doesn't it make sense it would do everything in its power to upset you MORE?

That's why it's so critical to let the Pig know you're willing to deal with ANY level of emotional discomfort without eating Slop. When you sever the connection between emotional upset and overeating, you also cut the fuel line which the emotional upset runs on in the first place. A funny thing then happens: You find you weren't quite as upset as you thought you were!

So yes, you may have some depression, anger, stress, loneliness, sadness, anxiety, etc. to deal with, but it may not be as bad as you think.

It turns out the BEST coping mechanism may be an authoritative declaration that henceforth YOU are in control, not your Pig. And you certainly aren't going to let the Pig binge anymore because you have "feelings."

All this aside, if you need a hug, I've got one for you! I'm not arguing for us to be less compassionate towards ourselves or others—to the contrary. If you need a hug, I've got one for you! What I AM saying is that it's worth considering whether whining about uncomfortable feelings is just your Pig's way of putting off the decision to stop over-eating, and whether the Pig might be escalating the drama in an effort to get more Slop. It's worth considering. What if I'm right?

» **12C QUESTION) How do you define Pig Squeal?** Please write your detailed answer below.

_____

_____

_____

_____

_____

_____

_____

_____

_____

_____

_____

_____

(Next Page Please)

» **12C ANSWER)** Pig Squeal is any thought, feeling, image, or impulse inside your head which suggests you will ever break your Food Plan between now and the day you die. By defining it this way AND ensuring the Food Rules on your Food Plan are crystal clear, you ensure you can always immediately distinguish the Pig's thoughts from your own. For example, if I will never eat chocolate again, what can my Pig possibly say and/or do which I wouldn't immediately recognize as Squeal?

The corollary to this definition is that each and every thought, feeling, image, and/or impulse which suggests you will STAY on your Food Plan is YOU. We aggressively separating our constructive, human selves from our destructive impulses and urges. We clearly define our own identity separate and apart from the Pig. And because the Pig is then—*by definition*—a 110% DESTRUCTIVE constellation of thoughts, feelings, images, and impulses, it becomes clear why we can't think of it as a cute pet and/or inner wounded child we are to nurture back to health. The Pig is a sociopathic entity which we unfortunately must learn to live with inside us, locked away in the mental "Cage" we have constructed for it for all eternity.

» **12D QUESTION) True or False? Food addiction is a disease.** Support your answer below in detail please.

» **12D ANSWER) False!** Never Binge Again asserts that food addiction is absolutely not a disease but rather just a very bad, very well ingrained habit which results from a healthy appetite corrupted by industry. This doesn't mean everyone should eat everything in moderation as there are some food-like-substances engineered by industry which are just too strongly pleasurable for some people to eat without abandon. What it does mean is that with focus and determination you have the power to change ANY habits. You are NOT helpless and powerless.

As of late there are some neurological studies being promoted as evidence for the disease model. But what these studies show is only that there are demonstrable areas of the brain *(mostly in the nucleus accumbens)* that "light up" differently for addicts vs. non-addicts in the alcohol space when they see alcohol, for example. Similar research shows these same areas light up in taxi drivers' brains when they are shown a taxi. Does that mean taxi driving is a disease too? Or is what we are seeing just brains doing what brains are supposed to do—adapt and change to whatever the greatest source of reward is in the environment. We can understand what we are seeing in the neurological correlate of a strong habit, and that's all.

There is also no demonstrable pathogen which causes overeating. If you lock someone with the disease of tuberculosis in a cell their symptoms will continue to get worse. If you lock someone with food addiction in a cell and feed them 3 healthy meals per day, they immediately get better.

» **12E – QUESTION) Which is easier, ruthlessly sticking to a rule that says "I will never eat chocolate on a weekday again" or becoming a person who doesn't eat chocolate during the week?** Justify your answer in as much detail as you can please.

_____

_____

_____

_____

_____

_____

» **12E – ANSWER)** Identity change is much easier in the long run than "white knuckling" adherence to your rules. For example, most people reading this would probably never steal a waitress' tip from the table at a diner, even if they were sure not to get caught. Why? Because being a law-abiding citizen has become a strong part of their identity. Unless you think of yourself as a thief it doesn't take willpower not to take that money. Stealing isn't even an option.

Similarly, becoming a person who doesn't eat chocolate is much easier than focusing on the rule "I will never eat chocolate again." We need the rule to get there, but the ultimate aim is to let it become part of your new identity. You need to be willing to become that person, even if you might make mistakes along the way. Character trumps willpower. When your character is clear, your decisions are easy.

» **12F – QUESTION) True or False? You must be forever vigilant and aware in order to remain on your Food Plan or else you will eventually Binge.** State and justify your answer below.

_____

_____

_____

_____

_____

_____

_____

_____

_____

_____

_____

_____

_____

» **12F – ANSWER) False.** You'll need to be vigilant for a few months in the beginning while you craft and experiment with your Food Plan, and then again any time you change and/or add a new Food Rule. But because the idea is to allow your Food Rules to become part of your new identity you will NOT need to be vigilant forever. It's kind of like learning how to drive. In the beginning you have to put in a serious effort to learn the rules of the road, practice your skills, and become comfortable on the highway, etc. But thereafter you just "know" what to do and you can listen to music, talk to a friend on a hands-free phone, etc. You kind of go into autopilot and navigate your way to the next destination. Another metaphor is getting a plane into the air. It requires an extraordinary amount of fuel to get off the runway and attain a cruising altitude, but thereafter only a fraction of that to get to its destination.

There's a very important principle underlying the above which may not be immediately obvious: **In Never Binge Again we cultivate confidence, not fear!** This is in sharp contrast to addiction treatment programs which suggest you must always stay frightened of a "chronic, mysterious, progressive, and powerful disease against which there is no human defense."

At every juncture we are looking to show our Pig we know we are stronger than it is. The idea one must stay constantly vigilant or else the Pig will get you is nothing more than fuel for the Squeal *"I'm just going to lay in wait until it's my time again. You can do your silly Food Plan for a while. But in the end, I rule the roost. You'll see!"* – Your Pig.

This means we don't require sponsors and accountability. We are not dependent little children who can't be trusted on their own, we are independent, strong adults who are putting a bad habit behind us.

Similarly, we don't have to hide and lock up all the junk food in the house because we can't be trusted. We don't have to avoid coffee shops, bakeries, etc. We choose to fully engage in life, not cower in the corner because we're terrified something might "trigger" us and "make" us Binge.

We also don't announce publicly how many days, weeks, months, or years it's been that we've been behaving well with food. We just behave, that's all.

There's one exception to this: In the beginning it's OK to rely on some tools as a kind of set of training wheels to get you started on your new journey. It can help to take another route home from work for a month or two if you've been regularly stopping somewhere on your main route to get Slop. Or to put the potato chips in another cupboard for the kids only. Or to work with someone for accountability for the first month or two. Research does show that creating a kind of cocoon of protection can help your new habits grow in safety. But eventually—*in the not too distant future*—those training wheels will have to come off or your Pig will see it as weakness. Hope that makes sense!

Post Assessment

What's changed?

Before finalizing our work together in this book, let's do a quick assessment of where you stand with your eating now, after having done the exercises. First, enter your starting food problem score from Go back to www.HowBigIsMyFoodProblem.com again, take the three minute quiz, then write your score below. *(TAKE THE QUIZ AND WRITE DOWN YOUR SCORE BELOW):*

→ **STARTING FOOD PROBLEM SCORE:** ____ *(Re-write it here from the beginning of the book)*

→ **ENDING FOOD PROBLEM SCORE:** ____ *(Write your score here)*

→ **CHANGE** ____ *(Enter starting score minus ending score here)*

Before You Go

Go someplace private and take three deep breaths while you hold this book to your heart once again. Then say out loud, with gusto "I WILL NEVER BINGE AGAIN!"

The latest copies of ALL my books are always available at www.NeverBingeAgainBooks. com The two most complimentary books to this workbook are 45 Binge Trigger Busters *(www.45BingeTriggers.com)* and 101 Best Food Rules *(www.101BestFoodRules.com).* If you specifically struggle with a *nighttime* overeating problem then you should also read "An End to Nighttime Overeating" *(www.StopEatingAtNight.com)* These books are also all available for Kindle, in paperback, and on Audible.com.

I also offer a coaching program via www.NeverBingeAgainCoaching.com

And there is a reader's forum at www.NeverBingeAgainForum.com

Made in the USA
Columbia, SC
05 May 2020